Managing
Alternative Pollinators

A Handbook for Beekeepers, Growers, and Conservationists

Written by

Eric Mader
Pollinator Outreach Coordinator
The Xerces Society Pollinator Conservation Program

Marla Spivak
Professor of Entomology
University of Minnesota

Elaine Evans
Author of *Befriending Bumble Bees*

With a Foreword by

Mace Vaughan
Conservation Director
The Xerces Society for Invertebrate Conservation

Sustainable Agriculture Research and Education (SARE)
Plant and Life Sciences Publishing (PALS)

Produced with support from:
The U.S. Department of Agriculture's Sustainable Agriculture Research and Education (SARE) Program
The University of Minnesota Department of Entomology
The Xerces Society Pollinator Conservation Program

NRAES–186
February 2010

ISBN 978-1-933395-20-3

Library of Congress Cataloging-in-Publication Data

Mader, Eric, date
Managing alternative pollinators : a handbook for beekeepers, growers, and conservationists /
Eric Mader, Marla Spivak, Elaine Evans ; with foreword by: Mace Vaughan.
　　p. cm. -- (SARE handbook ; 11) (NRAES ; 186)
ISBN 978-1-933395-20-3
1. Bee culture. 2. Bumblebees. 3. Mason bees. 4. Megachilidae. 5. Pollinators. I. Spivak,
Marla. II. Evans, Elaine, 1969- III. Natural Resource, Agriculture, and Engineering Service. IV.
Title. V. Series: NRAES (Series) ; 186.
SF523.M24 2010
638'.1--dc22

2009021044

Plant and Life Sciences Publishing (PALS)
Cooperative Extension
34 Plant Science Building
Ithaca, New York 14853
Phone: (607) 255-7654
Fax: (607) 254-8770
E-mail: PALSPUBLISHING@CORNELL.EDU
Web site: HTTP://PALSPUBLISHING.CALS.CORNELL.EDU/

Printed July 2014

Contents

Foreword

This book could not have come at a better time. We stand at a crossroads, where honey bee losses and rental rates for pollination are on the rise, research is expanding our knowledge of native bees' role in crop pollination, and growers are looking for pollination alternatives to improve crop security. Herein lies the heart of this book: It is a technical resource that brings together the latest advances in native and introduced bee management with a big-picture perspective on how to manage a farm for these pollinators' greatest success.

Pollinators are essential to our environment. Seventy percent of the world's flowering plants, including more than two-thirds of the world's crop species, rely on pollinators to reproduce. The fruits and seeds from these crops are necessary for 30 percent of the foods and beverages we consume, and include the most nutritious and interesting parts of our diet: apples, watermelon, blueberries, carrots, broccoli, and almonds to name but a few. We also count on pollinators for the beef and dairy products that come from cattle raised on alfalfa. In 2000, growers in the United States were paid close to $20 billion for insect-pollinated crops. According to estimates, managed and wild native bee species, as well as nonnative leafcutter and mason bees, are responsible for close to a quarter of this value; honey bees are responsible for the rest.

But now the honey beekeeping industry is in crisis. During the past 50 years, we have witnessed an almost 50 percent decline in the number of managed honey bee colonies in the United States. This trend is a result of stagnant honey prices in the 1970s and 1980s, combined in the past two decades with a barrage of new pests and diseases introduced from Europe, Asia, and potentially elsewhere. Most recently, and most alarmingly, the beekeeping community is facing Colony Collapse Disorder, where for still unknown reasons, worker bees simply abandon the hive. All these problems, known and mysterious, have led to beekeeper-reported losses of 30 percent during the 2006–2007 season and 35 percent during the 2007–2008 season.

With such sustained declines, beekeepers are going out of business. It can no longer be safely assumed that honey bees will provide all of farmers' future pollination needs. At the same time, research emerges every year about the role alternative pollinators, managed and wild, are playing in agriculture. Scientists from New Jersey to California and Michigan to Texas have demonstrated that wild native bees play a role in crop pollination. Other researchers continue to experiment with new species of managed native bees and the additional floral resources needed to support their successful reproduction.

All this work, however, raises concerns about how we manage our farm landscapes. The continuing trend toward larger monocultures, insecticide use, and the concomitant lack of habitat—particularly a decline in the number and diversity of flowering plants available when crops are not in bloom—creates a landscape where few crop pollinators can survive.

To diversify our pollinators, we must better understand how to manage a variety of bee species as well as the habitat that supports them and their wild counterparts. We cannot expect our natives to perform if we don't consider and provide for all of their habitat needs. For example, cherry and apple orchards might bloom for only three or four weeks, but mason bees are active as adults for six weeks or more. If flowers are not available outside of the crop bloom period, the dense concentration of foraging bees will run out of pollen and nectar sources. Their reproduction will not be enough to increase their managed populations.

Managing native bees also raises concerns. Moving them, for example, significantly increases the risk of spreading diseases or pests from one part of the country to another. These diseases may impact not only other managed bees but also their wild counterparts. As we increase our use of managed native bees, we need to exercise greater care and caution and develop regional varieties to help mitigate this potential problem.

In the coming years, honey bees will continue to be critically important for production agriculture. To improve the sustainability and security of farming in the United States, however, it is important for growers to diversify the pollinators upon which they rely. It also might be time for beekeepers to diversify their own operations and expand their management to native bees. This book provides the necessary tools for growers, beekeepers, and other agricultural professionals to do just that. Perhaps the silver lining of Colony Collapse Disorder is its wake-up call to invest time, research, and energy into new managed pollinators and new ways of looking at farm management for the betterment of all pollinators. We are being asked to picture a future in agriculture where even the most intensively managed almond orchards, cranberry bogs, and squash fields make room for flowering plants that complement blooming crops and have strategically placed hives of honey bees, tubes of leafcutters, boxes of bumble bees, and natural habitat that provides a home for wild native bees.

Mace Vaughan
Conservation Director
The Xerces Society for Invertebrate Conservation

To Our Readers

We assume you are like most people we know who are interested in bees and pollination: You are very practical and creative. Adept at learning with your hands, you prefer to be outdoors. You use books to answer questions that arise in the process of getting something done. Indeed, we suspect that many of you won't read this book cover to cover but will instead turn directly to the chapter that offers salient information. In the end, it's not important how you navigate this book. We simply want you to become inspired to rear alternative pollinators—bumble bees, mason bees, leafcutter bees, and others—for the pollination of crops and floral landscapes.

We urge you to be careful stewards of the pollinators we describe in this book. Most are in decline. Rearing bees can be a double-edged sword: It can be a huge service to an ecosystem by increasing the number of bees for pollination, but it can also move bees out of their native ranges and spread lethal diseases. We encourage you to foster the most sustainable, sanitary, and sensible practices possible.

We are adamant only about certain things:

—Whenever possible, rear only pollinators from your area. Do not ship bees across state or national borders without careful consideration.
—Mass production can lead to mass extinction. Use the most sanitary practices possible to discourage the development and spread of diseases and parasites.
—When rearing any type of bee, avoid the use of antibiotics, pesticides, and other treatments as much as possible.
—Always remember that careful and thoughtful bee management can affect our food systems and environment in profoundly important ways.

This book is unique for two reasons. First, to our knowledge, it is the only book of its kind to describe, in-depth, rearing and management practices for multiple alternative bee species. Other great books cover management of individual species, and we encourage you to check them out.

Second, this book combines scientific research with years of practical beekeeping experience. We've heard that our writing style is "folksy." This is intentional. We've spent plenty of time wearing white lab coats and writing on clipboards; but learning how to manage bees also requires a lot of time spent driving dusty roads in battered pickup trucks littered with beef jerky wrappers. Beekeeping is part science, part art; part theoretical, part practical. We have tried to synthesize that knowledge in language that bridges those dichotomies.

Researchers across the country are constantly making new discoveries. Part of your responsibility as a beekeeper is to stay on top of these findings. Additional resources listed in the back of this book will help you do that.

Another responsibility is to be an astute observer of your bees. Local environmental conditions have a tremendous effect on insect populations. The management systems described herein might need to be modified accordingly.

Beekeepers are generally a tremendously diverse, highly individualistic group of people. In our experience, however, the one thing most successful bee people have in common is good record keeping. Therefore, our final recommendation is that you keep a journal, noting the emergence time of your bees each year, the corresponding bloom times of crops and wild plants, parasite problems, weather, and management activities. Over time, patterns will emerge, and you can adapt your practices accordingly.

No doubt you will encounter challenges this book doesn't prepare you for. That's part of beekeeping. Ultimately, figuring out these mysteries is what makes working with bees so rewarding.

We wish you the best of luck with alternative pollinators. Keep us updated on your progress!

— Marla Spivak, Eric Mader, and Elaine Evans

1 The Business of Pollination

Marla Spivak, PhD, *Professor of Entomology, University of Minnesota*

Eric Mader, *Pollinator Outreach Coordinator, the Xerces Society for Invertebrate Conservation*

Nature is no longer a free commodity when it comes to crop pollination. As we increase crop acreage requiring insect pollination, bees must be mass reared to meet demand. We cannot rely on natural populations of bees and other pollinators for large crops because there are simply not enough out there. Through our land use, we have decreased natural nesting sites and the diversity of plants that support our native and introduced pollinators. Even just a couple acres of a fruit or vegetable crop can require either rearing and maintaining sufficient bees on the property or paying to have bees introduced (figure 1.1). Pollination is a business, and growers who need bees must calculate their cost and value into the operating budget (see sidebar, page 2).

The economic value of bees, all bees, as pollinators is difficult to estimate. For example, data are sorely lacking on the numbers and distribution of native bees throughout the United States, so it is difficult to calculate their exact contribution to pollination. Based on the best available economic modeling, we know that native bees contribute at least 3 billion dollars annually to US agriculture. We know they are vital and of immense value. Pollination of home gardens and natural landscapes, for example, is mostly done "for free" by native species of bees and managed honey bees.

It is slightly easier to estimate the numbers and value of honey bees supplied by beekeepers. Dr. Roger Morse and Dr. Nick Calderone of Cornell University offer the best estimate available, which they based on 1998 information from USDA's National Agricultural Statistics Service (NASS). We know the NASS survey statistics are inadequate, but they are the best we have. Morse and Calderone also conducted interviews with beekeepers, extension personnel and researchers, and in their 2000 publication concluded that "... the value of the increased yield and quality achieved through pollination by honey bees

Basil Furgala

Figure 1.1 Honey bee hives placed near a sunflower field needing pollination. The estimated annual value of bee pollination to the US sunflower industry is $312 million.

alone was $14.6 billion," a 57 percent increase from a previous estimate published in 1989. They attribute 20 to 25 percent of this increase to inflation, the rest to more people needing more pollinated food. The point: All bees provide an enormous service to our diet and landscape. They are invaluable and should command our attention and respect.

The Case for a Diversity of Bees

The greater the diversity of bees, the better the pollination. Honey bees are often considered the most important crop pollinator due to their sheer numbers. They live in large colonies requiring copious amounts of pollen and nectar for nourishment. Each honey bee colony contains about 30,000 bees, with a range of 10,000 to 60,000 bees, depending on the time of the year. They cover large territories when they forage, often flying 2 miles (~3.2 kilometers) or more. Through their dance language, they recruit each other to good nectar and pollen sources, and make it possible for a large number of bees to quickly find blooming flowers. They are always scanning the landscape for additional patches of flowers that bloom at different times of day to provide dietary diversity and quality. Other bee species may not have the numeric advantage of honey bees, but they have distinct traits that make them more efficient pollinators of many crops.

Different bees have different body sizes, tongue lengths, means of extracting pollen, dietary preferences, weather preferences, and life cycles. Different bees also have different foraging patterns: For example, honey bees tend to fly down a tree row while native bees often zigzag between rows ensuring cross-pollination. As another example, bumble bees are able to extract pollen through a process called buzz-pollination (see chapter 5, page 46), whereas honey bees are not able to do this. A combination of bumble bees and honey bees on cranberries would ensure that this native plant receives efficient pollination from a buzz-pollinating native bee and complete coverage of the flowers throughout the expansive bogs by the populous honey bee colonies. Having a diversity of bees means having the right tool for all occasions.

Take weather preferences. Honey bees will not forage much when the temperature drops below 55°F

POLLINATION COSTS PER ACRE, A SPECIES-BY-SPECIES COMPARISON

The number of managed bees needed to pollinate an acre of flowers depends on factors such as crop type, field size, availability of wild pollinators, time of year, and which bee species you intend to manage.

Careful analysis and ongoing field observations over several seasons may be necessary to make sense of your particular situation. Even so, many extension agencies and grower organizations have consistent recommended stocking rates for bees. Standard per-acre rates, where wild pollinators are absent, often are one to two honey bee hives, four bumble bee hives, 20,000 leafcutter bees, or 250 female mason bees (for tree fruits). The per-hectare rates are approximately 2.5 to 5 honey bee hives, 10 bumble bee hives, 50,000 leafcutter bees, or 620 mason bees.

The cost of maintaining these bees includes both one-time up-front costs for equipment, and annual ongoing maintenance expenses. Exact amounts vary depending on quality and type of equipment, and how intensively the bees are managed (with medications, nutritional supplements, etc.). Table 1.1 on page 3 shows several average-cost scenarios employing neither the best nor worst management practices for each species. Under optimal conditions, annual maintenance costs can be offset or even negated by hive products such as honey, wax, or the sale of excess bees.

(12.8°C), when it is raining or even drizzling, or when the winds are stronger than 20 to 25 mph (32 to 40 kph). In contrast, mason bees and bumble bees will forage in inclement weather. Almond growers prefer to have the insurance of 2 honey bee colonies per acre (~ 5 colonies per hectare) rather than just 1 colony per acre (~2.5 colonies per hectare) because

Table 1.1
Pollination Costs for Various Bee Species

COST OF TWO HONEY BEE COLONIES		
ITEM EXPENSES	INITIAL START-UP	ONGOING ANNUAL
Hive boxes, frames, and miscellaneous equipment	$500	
Package bees	$120	
Queen bees		$30
Supplemental sugar syrup feeding		$24
Pollen substitute		$14
Minimal medications (Fumagillin, Api-guard, etc.)		$80
TOTAL	$620	$148

COST OF 20,000 LEAFCUTTER BEES		
ITEM EXPENSES	INITIAL START-UP	ONGOING ANNUAL
One homemade plywood nest shelter	$50	
Five Styrofoam nest blocks	$50	$50
Five cardboard incubation trays	$50	$20
One mechanical cell extractor	$2000	
Two gallons of dormant bee cells	$100	
Incubation and refrigeration costs	+	+
TOTAL	$2250+	$70+

COST OF FOUR BUMBLE BEE COLONIES		
ITEM EXPENSES	INITIAL START-UP	ONGOING ANNUAL
Four annual hives from commercial producer		$450
TOTAL	$0	$450

COST OF 250 FEMALE MASON BEES		
ITEM EXPENSES	INITIAL START-UP	ONGOING ANNUAL
750 dormant cocoons (assumes 250 females)	$600	
Commercially available nest blocks (500 holes)	$300	$60
Paper nest inserts	$50	$60
Incubation and refrigeration costs	+	+
TOTAL	$950+	$120+

+ indicates that the cost of incubation and refrigeration is not included. These costs will be minimal the first year. The bulk of expenses for incubation and refrigeration will be incurred in year 2 when the beekeeper has a larger population that needs to be maintained for a full season. The expenses will vary depending on the situation.

it often rains during almond bloom, and sufficient bees for sunny-day foraging is critical. It would be beneficial for almond growers to place nesting blocks of mason bees nearby to ensure pollination on days when honey bees don't fly. A combination of mason bees and honey bees on almonds and apples may reduce the need to have 2 honey bee colonies per acre (~5 colonies per hectare).

One caution: Native bees can be reared to relieve some of the burden from the honey bees and their keepers. But it is very important to respect the native bees' distribution and life cycle. Native bees are well adapted to the regions of the United States where they live. If they are mass-reared and shipped to regions outside their native range for pollination, there is a risk of also transferring diseases and parasites. Further, they may out-compete, and ultimately cause the demise of, local species. Incorporating native bees into the business of pollination can have distinct benefits, but we must use this tool wisely.

Pollination Costs and Benefits: Almonds

An amazing example of the business of pollination comes from the almond industry. Currently, 615,000 acres (~250,000 hectares) of almonds are grown in the central valley of California. This crop is 100 percent dependent on bee pollination; bees *must* be present for the trees to produce nuts. Growers rent 2 colonies of honey bees per acre (~5 colonies per hectare) to ensure commercial nut set, which means that 1.2 million healthy colonies of honey bees need to be placed in the orchards by mid-February to satisfy pollination requirements. In 2010, it is projected that there will be 750,000 acres (~300,000 hectares) of almonds in bloom, which will require 1.5 million colonies. That is a mind-boggling number, especially considering that an estimated two million colonies are currently available (2008) to be transported for pollination in the United States.

Where do the almond growers obtain all these honey bees? An estimated half-million colonies are located year-round in California, and the rest are trucked in by professional beekeepers from as far away as Florida and Maine. These migratory beekeepers are the unsung heroes of agriculture: They are under extreme pressure to supply sufficient

Basil Furgala

Figure 1.2 Honey bee hives being loaded onto a truck. Migratory beekeeping is a highly mechanized business.

honey bees to meet the pollination demands of today's large-scale crops (figure 1.3). Beekeepers love bees, being outdoors, and hard work (figure 1.2).

Currently, a beekeeper receives up to $150 per colony to pollinate almonds. If a beekeeper moves 2,000 colonies into the orchards, he or she can gross $300,000. That sounds lucrative, but most beekeepers net only five to ten percent of their gross. The extraordinary amount of requisite time, labor, and supplies greatly narrow the profit margin.

What are a beekeeper's operating costs? It depends largely on fuel costs and whether the bees are being shipped across state lines. Approximately 400 colonies can be placed on one flatbed semi-trailer, depending on how heavy the colonies are. Fuel costs depend on the distance the bees need to be trucked. The bees need to be healthy before, during, and after they are moved.

The logistics and expenses for a beekeeper transporting honey bee colonies from out of state to the California almond orchards are more complicated than for in-state beekeepers (figure 1.4). First, California requires an apiary inspector from the state Department of Agriculture to certify that the colonies are disease free before they can enter the state. Certification fees vary from state to state. For example, inspectors check bee shipments for imported fire ants. Loads of bees can be rejected if they contain the ants on the underside of pallets or anywhere on the equipment.

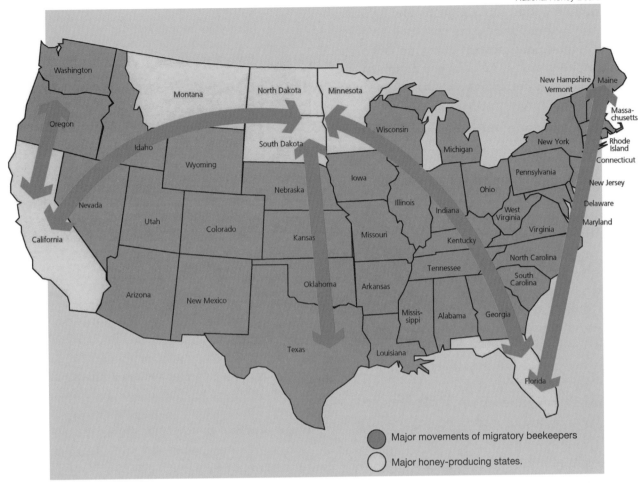

Major movements of migratory beekeepers

Major honey-producing states.

Figure 1.3 Some migratory routes of America's beekeepers.

Note: The major honey producing states are shown in yellow. Arrows show the path of some migratory beekeeping operations. For example, beekeepers on the East Coast may move colonies to the Northeast for blueberry and cranberry pollination and a variety of other crops, and to the South to produce honey from citrus. Some beekeepers in the Midwest may move their colonies to California for almond pollination, then return to produce large honey crops from clover, alfalfa, canola, and basswood. Other midwestern beekeepers may move their colonies to Texas and other southern states to produce queen bees and to increase their colony numbers by making "divides."

Another major expense is incurred if the beekeeper decides to pay someone to truck the bees to California and then someone else to "bee-sit" the colonies. Sometimes the beekeeper and his family move to California, which also involves a host of potentially costly and complex logistical decisions, such as two homes and enrolling children in two schools. In both cases, the colonies may be stockpiled in one or more locations, sometimes with 1,000 colonies in one lot waiting to be moved into the almonds. The colonies must be given supplemental feedings of sugar syrup and pollen substitute to keep bees nourished and well populated until almond bloom.

Figure 1.4 Honey bees trucked in for the California almond bloom. Bees are trucked from as far away as Florida and flown in from Australia.

What is the gain to the almond grower? Everything. Without bees, there are no nuts. One estimate says almond growers spend about 20 percent of their operating budgets (variable farming costs) on renting bees for pollination. These costs seem like a small price to pay given the alternative without bees. As almond acreage increases, more bee colonies will need to be trucked in from all points to satisfy a demand that is beginning to far outpace supply. In recent years, beekeepers have started importing "package bees" (mini-starter colonies) from Australia, which means we are now importing the service of pollination. In our modern landscape, economics is driving nature—but with diminishing returns. The potential importation of bee diseases and susceptible bee stocks from other countries, for example, creates a murky economic forecast.

Not too many years ago, when orchards were smaller, bees could build up strength on the high-quality protein of almond pollen. The bees would grow naturally into full-sized colonies by the time the almonds finished blooming three to four weeks later. Then the colonies would be strong enough to move into citrus orchards to make a crop of orange blossom honey. Now that almond growers only pay full price for full strength by the bloom's start, the almond market is setting an unsustainable rhythm for many of our nation's honey bees. If we're not careful, the business of pollination can drive our pollinators out of the business of life.

Pollination Costs and Benefits: Cranberries

A very different example of the business of pollination comes from the cranberry industry. Cranberries are a native crop cultivated primarily in Wisconsin, Massachusetts, New Jersey, Oregon, and Washington. More than 39,000 acres (~15,800 hectares) of cranberries were harvested in the United States in 2005, a mere six percent of the total almond acreage in California's Central Valley. Honey bees are not the most efficient bee in extracting pollen from a cranberry blossom (figure 1.5). But when the berries are grown over large acreages, they are the only pollinators with populations large enough to cover the entire crop. Bumble bees have longer tongues and because they can also buzz-pollinate, are much more

Figure 1.5 A honey bee pollinating a cranberry flower. While not the most efficient pollinator of cranberries, honey bees are often used because not enough wild pollinators are available.

efficient cranberry pollinators, on a flower-by-flower basis. It is difficult and very expensive, however, to obtain enough bumble bees to pollinate the crop.

Cranberries bloom in late June. This means that renting bees for cranberry pollination (as well as for pumpkin and other vine crops that blossom in midsummer) is usually at the expense of a honey crop the bees could make elsewhere from clover, alfalfa, and other wildflowers blooming at the same time.

A survey conducted by the Wisconsin Agricultural Statistics Service revealed that more than 17,000 acres (~6900 hectares) of cranberries were harvested in the state in 2005. That year, 76 percent of Wisconsin growers rented, on average, 1.8 honey bee colonies per acre (~4.5 colonies per hectare) at $50 per colony. Seven percent of the growers in 2005 rented honey bee colonies and purchased disposable bumble bee colonies, while six percent purchased only bumble bees. The survey also indicated that most cranberry growers had contracted the same beekeeper for an average of five years, and more than 72 percent were satisfied with the service. Just more than half of the colonies were inspected for colony strength that year, which means the grower trusted the beekeeper to rent them strong, populous colonies. It is not clear how many of the beekeepers signed pollination contracts to ensure payment.

The following is a first-hand example of the impact of honey bees and local native bees on cranberry pollination in Wisconsin. In 1999, a grower introduced 3 honey bee colonies per acre (7.4 colo-

Woodworth Honey and Bee Co. had its roots in Iowa in 1937 when Wendell (Woody) Woodworth caught a swarm of bees. In 1955, the Woodworths moved to North Dakota with 400 colonies in tow. For seven years, they maintained bees in North Dakota year-round and replaced colonies that died during the long hard winter with "package bees" purchased from California. In 1962, Woody began moving his colonies to Idabel, Okla. for the winter, and in 1972 moved his operation even deeper south to Nacogdoches, Tex., where the early spring allowed him to increase the number of colonies and raise new queen bees before bringing them back to North Dakota to make honey in the summer. By 1979, Woody had 6,000 colonies. He sold one-third of the colonies to one of his sons and another third to his son, Brent, and Brent's wife, Bonnie, keeping the remainder for himself. In 1991, Brent and Bonnie took their first load of bees to California to pollinate almonds.

Today, Brent and Bonnie have 3,800 colonies and their operation is run almost exclusively between North Dakota and California. They pay a professional trucker to haul 3,200 colonies to California in October and November. The colonies are situated in the Central Valley in holding apiaries sometimes containing thousands of colonies. They must provide supplementary feedings of sugar syrup and pollen and medications to control diseases and mites so colonies are strong enough for almond pollination by mid-February.

When the almonds finish blooming in late March, Brent and Bonnie used to ship 6 to 8 loads of bees (at around 400 to 450 colonies per load) to Yakima Valley in Washington to pollinate apples. But the apple growers wanted the bees moved out as soon as the

Bonnie Woodworth

Brent and Bonnie Woodworth.

apples stopped blooming, in early April, too early to move colonies back to cold, flowerless North Dakota. So now they ship only two loads to Washington and maintain the bulk of their colonies in Central California where they split their colonies to introduce new queens and increase colony numbers before trucking them back to North Dakota in early May. They produce honey during the summer in North Dakota, primarily from clover, alfalfa and canola, averaging around 125 pounds per colony (~57 kilograms per colony). They sell their honey to Golden Heritage Foods, where it is bottled and retailed. The bees are treated for diseases and mites, and by late October are trucked back to California to repeat the cycle.

The Woodworths estimate they net around 10 percent of their gross. In recent years, 65 to 70 percent of their income has come from pollination, the rest from honey. In former years, it was the opposite. Since 2000, however, the price per colony for pollinating almonds tripled and their business followed the boom and bloom. Their biggest expense is labor: It is difficult to find people willing and able to put up with beekeeping's hard work and stings.

The Woodworths are adamant about their biggest challenge: ensuring their colonies are populous and healthy enough by mid-February to meet almond growers' criteria. Bees' natural tendency is to hunker down for winter and build up colony strength cautiously in spring until flowers are in full bloom. Nowadays, almond growers pay top dollar only if colonies have more than eight frames of bees per colony by mid-February. Bees must be stimulated early with supplemental feedings to reach that kind of strength at that time of year.

nies per hectare) onto his cranberry property. The next year, due to a market glut, the grower intentionally reduced his yield by not introducing honey bee colonies. Researcher Elaine Evans compared his yield in one particular bed with and without honey bees. With honey bees present, the individual cranberries weighed on average 0.056 ounces (1.6 grams), the normal weight of a well-pollinated cranberry. Without honey bees, the average cranberry weighed only 0.028 ounces (0.8 grams), half the weight. Yield is measured in biomass (barrels), so this grower certainly reached his goal to reduce yield.

Evans also observed honey bee and native bee visitation on these beds. The year honey bees were introduced by the grower mentioned above, she found 34 honey bees per ~1080 square feet (100 square meters). The next year, when the grower did not introduce honey bees, she found zero honey bees foraging on the cranberry flowers. She found one to three native bumble bees per 100 square meters, and a smaller number of halictids, megachilids and other bees both years whether honey bees were present or not, indicating that these native pollinators are in cranberry beds, just not in high numbers.

Previous research by Dr. Jim Cane showed that bees must deposit a minimum of eight pollen grain "tetrads" on the stigma of the flower for an individual cranberry blossom to set fruit. Did the cranberry bed with a few native bees but no honey bees receive sufficient numbers of these pollen tetrads? During early and late bloom, when few blossoms were open on each flower stalk (called an "upright"), the flowers did receive at least eight tetrads. But during midbloom, when the majority of flowers are open, only 50 percent received sufficient pollen.

The lesson to be learned from this story is that there are too few native, naturally present bees to ensure fruit set and good berry weight. Large acreages need honey bees, or a combination of honey and bumble bees, to ensure that all flowers receive enough pollen grains, especially during midbloom.

Natural areas provide nesting sites and forage for native bees. So, native bee populations will be more prevalent when natural areas surround the cranberry property—or any cropland. When cropland is surrounded by agricultural or disturbed land, native bees have fewer nesting sites. Also, honey bees may prefer to forage on the disturbed land, especially if flowers there yield more nectar and pollen or if the bees are introduced before the crop blooms. All crops and locations are not equal: timing is important, knowledge key.

Other Crops

Beekeepers interested in supplying honey bees for any crop that requires pollination—for example, apples, blueberries, or pumpkins—should educate themselves about how and when the crop blooms and which bees besides honey bees can help (see table 1.2, page 10). Mason bees are excellent pollinators of apples, which bloom in early spring, often during inclement weather. Bumble bees and anthophorids with long tongues are excellent pollinators of blueberries, which have a long corolla (figure 1.6). Squash bees, *Peponapis* (figure 1.7) and *Xenoglossa*,

Jim Cane

Figure 1.6 Honey bees and bumble bees foraging on blueberry flowers.

A. Blueberry flowers have a long corolla, and the honey bee's tongue is too short to reach the nectar. As a result, honey bees may chew holes in the petals to sip nectar (left), bypassing the flower's reproductive structures.

B. Bumble bees (right) are strong enough to pry open the blueberry blossoms, and their long tongue can reach the flower's nectary. The vigorous shaking a foraging bumble bee gives the blossom ensures a lot of pollen transfer.

Jim Cane

Figure 1.7
A squash bee gathering nectar from a zucchini flower. Squash bees (*Peponapis* sp.) are native ground-nesting bees that specialize in pollinating squash, gourds, and other cucurbits.

are curcubit specialists and can outperform honey bees. These solitary, ground-nesting bees, however, cannot be managed or cultivated, but they are found throughout the United States, often in large numbers and on most flowering curcubits.

The beekeeper and grower should know the best time to introduce honey bees (before or just after bloom begins), what other bees can help, and which flowers yield sufficient nectar and pollen to maintain the large colonies (figure 1.8). Pumpkins, for example, only bloom in the morning and do not yield much nectar. Colonies will require large stores of honey or supplemental feed during and particularly after pumpkin bloom to stay strong and adequately nourished. A beekeeper and grower cannot assume that all flowers are equally profitable for bees. It helps if both beekeeper and grower think like a bee.

Mace Vaughan

Figure 1.8 Native (like this *Osmia aglaia*), and nonnative mason bees have been effectively managed for pollination of many fruit crops, such as tree fruits and berries. Shown here is a mason bee pollinating raspberry.

Pollination for Hire

Before World War II, beekeepers provided bees free to growers, whose land provided sufficient flowers before, during, and after crop bloom. In the late 1940s and early 1950s, beekeepers all over the United States realized they should be paid for the service; bees could be making profitable honey instead of pollinating crops. Beekeepers started asking for modest fees, sometimes only $0.50 per colony.

Today, while some beekeepers and growers use written contracts, many still consider the business of pollination a gentlemen's agreement. The grower and beekeeper mutually decide when the bees will be moved in and out, as well as colony placement and strength. Beekeepers trust that growers will not spray harmful pesticides while the bees are foraging, or at least will notify them if and when spraying will occur. Beekeepers trust there will be water available for the bees, preferably within one-quarter mile of the colony, as a colony requires up to 1 gallon (~4 liters) of water per day. Growers pay beekeepers an agreed-upon price, and at the end of the bloom they shake hands and say, "See you next year; same time, same place." Some growers pay the beekeeper 50 percent of the fee upon delivery; the other half when the bees are removed. If the grower is dissatisfied with the strength or performance of the colonies, the last payment can be reduced.

The gentlemen's agreement is fraught with miscommunication and problems. One way to avoid this is to work with a written contract, often developed by a broker, or middleman, who, for a cut of the pollination fees, negotiates prices and timing and placement of hives. Sometimes brokers inform growers how to protect the bees from harmful pesticide exposure. They sometimes also arrange for the beekeeper to provide more colonies if needed. Even with a broker, the beekeeper is usually responsible for collecting colony rental fees. If the grower doesn't pay, the beekeeper loses.

The broker or grower inspects a certain percentage of the beekeeper's colonies and determines the fee based on average colony strength. In almond pollination, a beekeeper may get paid by the average number of frames of bees per colony. One box holds nine to ten frames, and each colony is usually hived in two boxes. Beekeepers will not get paid for colonies that have five or fewer frames of bees; ten or more frames garner the best price. The colonies must have laying queens and at least five to seven frames of brood (eggs, larvae, and pupae).

For almonds, bee brokers are common, and a number of reputable brokers are available. For cranberries, blueberries, apples, or pumpkins, brokers are not often used, possibly because bee colony rental fees are not as high for these crops. Whether a middleman is used or not, a signed pollination contract between the grower and beekeeper is highly recommended. A handshake may seem like a more friendly way to do business, but a contract is binding and can ensure a long-lasting business relationship.

| | Table 1.2 | | | |
| | Managed Bees of Major Commercial Crops | | | |
CROP	HONEY BEES	BUMBLE BEES	LEAFCUTTER BEES	MASON BEES
Alfalfa	•		•	
Almond	•	•		•
Alsike clover	•			
Apples	•	•		•
Apricot	•	•		
Avocados	•			
Berseem clover	•			
Blackberries	•			
Blueberries	•	•	•	•
Borage	•	•	•	
Buckwheat	•			
Cantaloupe	•	•		
Canola	•		•	
Carrot	•	•	•	
Celeriac	•			
Celery	•			
Cherries	•	•		•
Chicory	•			
Cicer milkvetch	•			
Cole crops	•	•		
Cranberries	•	•	•	
Crimson clover	•			
Crown vetch	•		•	
Cucumber	•	•		
Currants	•	•		
Dewberries	•			
Dill	•			
Eggplant		•		
Fennel	•			
Garlic	•			
Gooseberries	•	•		
Hairy vetch	•		•	
Kenaf	•			
Kiwi	•	•		

Table 1.2
Managed Bees of Major Commercial Crops (continued)

CROP	HONEY BEES	BUMBLE BEES	LEAFCUTTER BEES	MASON BEES
Kohlrabi	•			
Lavender	•			
Leek	•			
Macadamia	•			
Mango	•			
Mint	•		•	
Muskmelon	•	•		
Mustard	•			
Nectarines	•			
Onion	•		•	
Parsley	•			
Parsnip	•			
Passion fruit	•			
Peaches	•	•		•
Pears	•	•		•
Persimmons	•			
Plums	•	•		•
Prunes	•			•
Pumpkin	•			
Radish	•			
Raspberries	•	•		•
Red clover		•		
Rutabaga	•			
Strawberries	•	•		•
Sunflower	•			
Sweet clover	•			
Sweet pepper		•		
Sweet vetch	•		•	
Tangerine	•			
Tomato		•		
Trefoil	•			
Turnips	•			
Watermelon	•			
White clover	•			
Zucchini	•	•		

Again, the biggest problem with verbal pollination agreements is miscommunication. Both beekeeper and grower can make assumptions about the timing of moving bees in and out of the crop, placement, access to the bees, availability of water, pesticide use, colony strength, and payment schedule. If intentions are not spelled out ahead of time, disaster can easily follow.

Pollination Contracts

A sample contract is included on page 13. A number of key points should be specified in a written contract between the beekeeper and grower, including:

- Rental fee and date payable
- Dates when the bees should be moved in and out of the crop
- Colony distribution within the crop and vehicle accessibility
- Strength of bee colonies (numbers of frames of bees and brood)
- Whether the colonies will be inspected for strength, by whom, and at whose expense
- Grower and/or pesticide applicator assurance to not use pesticides toxic to bees (see Appendice D, page 130)
- Grower agreement to notify beekeeper about other pesticide spraying in area
- Possible injury (stinging incidents) to growers and workers

- Who pays for vandalism or theft of colonies, or if colonies are destroyed by flood or other natural disaster
- Grower agreement to pay for extra movement of colonies into and out of the crop
- Grower agreement to provide right of entry to beekeeper for management of bees
- Beekeeper agreement to inspect bees before and during time in the orchard to maintain good condition for pollination
- Names, addresses, phone numbers, tax identification numbers/social security number

Some Final Words on Fees and Bees

Most beekeepers are paid rental fees to cover the costs of transporting and maintaining the colonies and to make a fair profit. Given bees' importance to pollination, it might make more sense for beekeepers to earn a share of crop fees, which gives them incentive to supply the best colonies to obtain the highest possible yield. Without bees, many fruit and vegetable blossoms would not set seed. At best, produce would be misshapen and fruits far less sweet. Even a slight drop in fruit and vegetable quality would lead to an economic loss, particularly in the US, where consumers expect perfectly shaped produce. Pollination is no longer a free commodity, and beekeepers should be paid well, certainly more than they currently are paid, for the invaluable service their bees provide.

Sample Pollination Contract

(From the Mid-Atlantic Apicultural Research & Extension Consortium. Publication 5.4. February 2000.)

This agreement is made _____ between _____
  (month/day/year)   (grower's name)

and_____
  (beekeeper's name)

1. TERM OF AGREEMENT. The term of this agreement shall be for the _____ growing season.
  (year)

2. RESPONSIBILITIES OF THE BEEKEEPER:

  a. The beekeeper shall supply the grower with _____ hives (colonies) of
  (number)

  honey bees to be delivered to the _____as follows:
  (orchard, field, etc)

  (Fill in the appropriate line or lines and cross out those that do not apply)

Approximate date of introduction _____

Number of days after written notice from the grower _____

Time in relation to the following amount of bloom _____

_____

Description of Location(s) _____

_____

  (For additional space attach a separate sheet dated and signed by both parties)

The beekeeper shall locate said bees in accordance with directions of the grower, or, if none are given, according to his judgment in providing the maximum pollination coverage.

  b. The beekeeper agrees to provide colonies of the following *minimum* standards;

  disease-free colonies with a laying queen as evidenced by brood:

  _____ frames with brood

  _____ frames covered with adult bees

  _____ pounds of honey stores or other food

  _____ story of hives

The beekeeper agrees to open and demonstrate the strength of colonies randomly selected by grower.

  c. The beekeeper agrees to maintain the bees in proper pollinating condition by judicious inspection and supering or honey removal as needed.
  d. The beekeeper agrees to leave the bee on the crop until:

  (Fill in the appropriate line or lines and cross out those that do not apply)

  Approximate date of removal _____.

  Number of days of written notice from grower _____ *(continued on page 14)*

Time in relation to amount of crop bloom _____

Other _____

3. RESPONSIBILITIES FOR THE GROWER:

a. The grower agrees to provide a suitable place to locate the hives. The site must be accessible to a truck and/or other vehicles used in handling and servicing the colonies. The grower shall allow the beekeeper entry on the premises whenever necessary to service the bees, and the grower assumes full responsibility for all loss and damage to his fields or crops resulting from the use of trucks or other vehicles in handling and servicing such colonies of honey bees.

b. The grower agrees not to apply pesticides toxic to bees to the crop while the bees are being used as pollinators nor immediately prior to their movement into the field or orchard if the residue would endanger the colonies.

c. The following pesticides, other agricultural chemicals, and methods of application are mutually agreed to be suitable while the bees are on the crop:

_____

_____

d. The grower also agrees to properly dispose of all pesticide solutions in such a manner that bees will not be able to contact the material while searching for a water source.

e. The grower agrees to give the beekeeper 48 hours' notice if hazardous materials not listed on this contract need to be applied. The cost of moving the bees away and back to the crop to prevent damage from toxic materials shall be borne by the grower.

f. The grower agrees to pay for _____ colonies of bees at the rate of
                              (number)

$_____ per colony. Payment shall be made to the beekeeper as follows: $_____
   (amount)   (amount)

per colony on delivery and the balance on or before _____ of said year.
                                               (date)

Additional moves or settings shall require $_____ per hive per move.
                                       (amount)

g. The grower agrees to provide adequate watering facilities for the bees if none are available within ½ mile (0.8 kilometers) of each colony used in pollinating the crop.

Signed: Date: _____

_____   _____
                     Grower   Beekeeper

Address _____   Address _____

_____   _____

Phone number _____   Phone number _____

2 The Status of the European Honey Bee in the US

Marla Spivak, PhD, *Professor of Entomology, University of Minnesota*

Honey bees are our pollination workhorses—and they are overworked. To understand why America's farmers need alternative pollinators, it is important to understand why honey bees are used so extensively for pollination and the hardships they and their keepers face in response to this demand. It is also important to heed lessons about the rewards and challenges of keeping honey bees healthy in our modern agricultural and urban environment so we do not make the same mistakes in rearing other bees. Given how critical bee pollination is to agriculture, we absolutely cannot take any bees for granted.

Although some information is given in this chapter on how to keep bees healthy with minimal chemical inputs, the following pages are intended to help readers understand the current plight of honey bees, not to provide a primer on beekeeping. Such information is well covered in other books (see Bibliography, page 149).

What Makes Honey Bees Great Pollinators?

Honey bees are great pollinators because they live in colonies with very large populations and require copious amounts of pollen to survive. A large, healthy colony can have up to 50,000 adult bees (figure 2.2). The queen can lay around 1,000 eggs per day, and each larva requires large amounts of protein-rich

Eric Mader

Figure 2.1 A honey bee gathering nectar from a borage flower. Despite their challenges, honey bees remain essential pollinators of agricultural crops and native wildflowers.

Gary Reuter

Figure 2.2 A healthy, populous colony. Honey bees construct their wax combs within movable wood or plastic frames provided by the beekeeper.

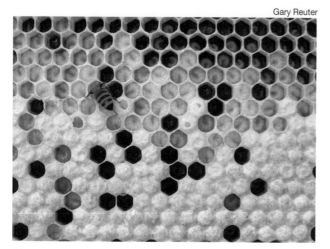

Figure 2.3 A honey bee comb with healthy larvae visible and pupae in waxed cap cells. Larvae are fed large amounts of brood food by nurse bees.

food for the first five days of its development (figure 2.3). This food, called royal jelly or brood food, is produced in glands located in the heads of young bees, and these glands develop in response to young bees consuming lots of pollen. They can store some pollen in the nest for times of dearth, but when the colony is really growing, the older bees must forage daily to support the growth and development of their enormous family. Honey bees will fly a remarkable 1 to 3 miles (1.6 to 4.8 kilometers) to reach the best pollen and nectar plants.

The biology of honey bees makes them excellent pollinators, but their numbers and health are in serious decline in the US. What are the events that led honey bees to this low point?

Honey bees were extinct in North and South America when *Apis mellifera* was introduced by European settlers in the 1600s—a 14 million-year-old fossil honey bee called *A. nearctica* found in Nevada indicates honey bees were once present. Before honey bees were introduced in the 1600s, native bee species were abundant and pollinated native plants. The most common of these included: sand or mining bees (in the family Andrenidae); plasterer bees (family Colletidae); sweat bees (family Halictidae); mason and leafcutter bees (Megachilidae); and bumble bees, carpenter bees and digger bees (all in the family Apidae). Honey bees (also in the family Apidae) thrived in the New World, particularly as we introduced non-native and invasive weedy plants.

As a honey bee colony prospered, it would outgrow the size of its manmade nest boxes and *swarm*, sending out half of the bees and the queen to initially bivouac before moving into and occupying a new nest site. Swarming is how honey bees propagate new colonies—how their population increases naturally. Swarms that survive the winter grow into another large colony the next year. The bees that remain in the natal nest rear a new queen bee and continue unhampered. Many of these swarms occupy tree and other cavities large enough to accommodate their populations and honey stores. These colonies are called wild or feral honey bee colonies, but in the US, feral honey bees originated as escapees from manmade equipment.

In the past, numbers of managed and feral honey bees, and other native bees, were sufficient enough to satisfy most pollination needs. If a farmer grew a few acres of a crop that required bees for pollination—such as apples or pumpkins—a beekeeper would bring a few colonies of honey bees to the area in exchange for a handshake. If a farmer grew 100 acres (40.5 hectares) of a crop that required pollination, a beekeeper would bring in enough colonies to supply 1 to 2 colonies per acre (2.5 to 5 colonies per hectare). In most cases, the bees thrived on the blooming crop and surrounding wildflowers—a beneficial situation for all involved.

In the last 50 years or so, crop sizes have increased dramatically and so has insecticide and herbicide use, which has altered the landscape in new and alarming ways. Crops are sprayed or dusted with compounds to control pest insects. Herbicides are used to eliminate weeds, which reduces the bees' food supply. Most farmers have stopped rotating their crops with clover and alfalfa, prime floral resources for bees, and instead use nitrogen fertilizers to replenish the soil. In most cases, modern developments have not been friendly to honey bees or our native bees.

Parasite Pressures

The 1980s marked the beginning of a precipitous and ongoing drop in honey bee populations. Two different parasitic mites were inadvertently introduced into the US, both of which live exclusively on honey bees and do not affect other bee populations.

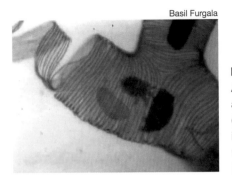

Basil Furgala

Figure 2.4
A honey bee's airway passage (tracheal tubes) infested with acarine tracheal mites (*Acarapis woodi*).

One microscopic mite, the tracheal mite *Acarapis woodi*, lives in the honey bees' breathing tubes (figure 2.4), piercing them to feed on the bee's blood, or *hemolymph*. If many bees in the colony are infested with tracheal mites, the adult worker force becomes weakened and sometimes dies. But these mites are relatively benign compared to the next mite that was introduced.

Varroa destructor is relatively large and can be seen with the naked eye. *Varroa* mites have a more complicated lifestyle than tracheal mites. These mites also feed on bee hemolymph on both adults and tender developing pupae. Fertile female mites ride around on the bodies of adult bees, eventually entering a cell containing a larva just ready to pupate. As the bee goes through the pupal phase, the mite and her developing offspring feed on the pupa's hemolymph.

Varroa does not kill the pupa outright, but weakens it. Pupae forced to share their blood and nutrient supply with a family of large mites become short-lived adults with compromised immune systems. The mites prefer to infest drone brood because the mites can produce more offspring in the longer developing drone pupae. However, *Varroa* has no compunction about infesting worker pupae, and when enough of the colony's worker force develops from parasitized pupae, the colony becomes weakened and eventually will die (see sidebar, below).

Controlling the mites has been approached differently, depending on the beekeeper and the mite. Strategies range from ignoring the mites to combating them with chemical treatments. In the US most beekeepers choose the chemical strategy. Chemical control of tracheal mites involves using menthol crystals. The vapors enter the bees' breathing tubes and kill the mites. Bees don't really like the intense odor of menthol in their colony, but the treatment seems relatively harmless. Interestingly, with time, most beekeepers have come to ignore tracheal mites, particularly as *Varroa* has become a more consuming problem. Ignoring tracheal mites allowed the bees time to develop their own defenses against it. Today, many colonies in the US demonstrate some resistance to these mites, and only in some regions is it

THE VARROA MITE

It should seem odd to the alert reader that obligate parasites such as *Varroa* mites would eventually kill off their host. After all, they cannot live on anything but honey bees and if they kill the host colony, they will die. But honey bees are maintained in apiaries, with many colonies in close proximity, and it is easy for mites to jump ship on a foraging bee and enter a neighboring colony and continue on. This movement of mites is called *horizontal transmission* and is the main mode of transmission of *Varroa* mites throughout the country. Fortunately, there are some locations, such as the Arnot forest in upstate New York, that host a small number of feral colonies spaced far enough apart in tree cavities that the mites cannot jump ship with ease. In this situation, the mites and bees have reached a tenuous equilibrium; the bees are weakened but the colonies do not die. The bees grow and eventually swarm, and this is how the mite gains access to new territory. This process of transmission of mites from mother to daughter colony is called *vertical transmission*, and it is a more sustainable situation for the bees and the mites. However, to pollinate large-scale crops, we need many, many colonies in one area, which inevitably and unfortunately leads to extreme horizontal transmission.

necessary for beekeepers to continue to use menthol to treat them.

Controlling *Varroa* is a different issue. It is not easy to ignore this creature. The size of a *Varroa* mite on a bee is relatively the same size as a dinner plate on a person (figure 2.5). Imagine having a mite on you that size! To keep colonies alive beekeepers have taken steps most never dreamed of: They became pesticide applicators. This is unusual because beekeepers are environmentalists by necessity. The health of their bees depends on a healthy environment. Beekeepers tend to be staunch opponents of reckless pesticide use on crops, especially compounds that potentially harm their foraging bees. But to keep producing honey and to provide healthy bees for pollination, they needed to control *Varroa*. Chemical companies and researchers rushed to the "rescue" and so began the insidious chemical treadmill process within honey bee colonies. The treadmill began with the registration of one compound, a synthetic pyrethroid, that was highly effective in controlling *Varroa* mites, and was followed by the development of resistance to the pyrethroid by the mite, so that a new compound from a different class of insecticides had to be registered, and so on. The honey bee industry is relatively small and not a profitable market to large chemical companies, so only one compound was registered for the first ten years, which did not allow beekeepers to rotate chemicals and forestall resistance by the mites to the compounds.

Nick Calderone

Figure 2.5 Varroa mites (*Varroa destructor*), are large reddish-brown external parasites that feed on the body fluids of immature and adult bees. Mites reduce the life span of bees and weaken their immune systems. They also transmit viruses from bee to bee.

We cannot blame the US beekeepers for turning to chemical control methods to keep their colonies alive. Their option was to let their colonies die and not fulfill pollination contracts. If honey bee populations were allowed to crash from the mites, what would happen to the 615,000 acres (~250,000 hectares) of almond trees in California that require bee pollination all at once? Or 1,000 acres (~400 hectares) of blueberries in Maine? Or, 100 acres (~40 hectares) of apples in Washington, or even 50 acres (~20 hectares) of pumpkins in Minnesota? The simple fact is that the American public would not have tolerated a reduced crop of bee-pollinated fruits and vegetables for the ten to twenty years it would have taken for the honey bee population to naturally evolve defenses against the mites and build up to pre-mite population levels. It was in the immediate interests of most people to keep our fruits and vegetables pollinated by honey bees so we could continue to purchase inexpensive, well-formed, and succulent produce.

What happens to the diseases and parasites of bees when so many colonies are placed in such high densities, such as in apiaries, or moved en masse by trucks and placed in holding yards until the crop is ready to bloom? The magnitude of the potential problem is astounding. We produce fruits and vegetables on a large scale, but the demand it places on honey bees is historically unprecedented and unsustainable. Honey bees are the pollination workhorse, and our agricultural practices force them to work themselves down to the nubbin.

Even if we did not grow such expansive acreages of fruits and vegetables that require bee pollination, another pressing question must be addressed: Are there sufficient wildflowers in our environment for bees to feed on? As we cover native wildflowers and weedy fields with lawns in the process of urban sprawl, and as we spray our highways and roadsides with herbicides to kill weeds, we diminish bee pasture. Bees thrive on flowers that we consider unkept and weedy. Just like humans, bees absolutely require a variety of amino acids from protein, which they obtain from a wide variety of flowers to maintain a balanced and healthy diet. A half-million acres (~200,000 hectares) of almond blossoms sounds like a lot of pollen and protein. But for bees, it is like eating nothing but chicken every day for a month.

Pesticide Problems

The problems that have led to the decline of honey bees, and all bees, are evident even on a small, seemingly innocuous scale. It is relatively easy to keep one or two colonies on a small farm or in a city or suburban lot alongside a garden and some fruit trees. The bees from these colonies will forage a mile or two from their colony and will help pollinate the neighborhood fruits, vegetables, and flowers. Urban beekeeping is a wholesome and helpful hobby and should be strongly promoted. But what if the neighbors decide to treat their garden plants with insecticides to kill off the unwanted insects? What if these chemicals have the potential to kill wanted insects —the beneficial bees?

How do we kill off pest insects while protecting bees? It may be impossible to convince your neighbor to let grubs kill his trees rather than using an insecticide. It also may not be possible to encourage the neighbor to use some bio-rational or other control measure that would not harm the bees. Reading the label on an insecticide to try to encourage our neighbor to choose a safe compound may or may not be helpful. Some very toxic insecticides that are sold to home gardeners do not include a warning that the chemicals are harmful to bees (and other beneficial insects). This lack of warning on insecticide labels for home and garden use is an alarming current state of affairs and should be remedied immediately.

Although a hobby beekeeper may avoid chemical use in his or her garden, bees fly far enough to pick up insecticides outside the garden or small farm. Sometimes bees bring back pollen into the nest that is contaminated with an insecticide. They may store this pollen and then eat it at a later date, suffering consequences months after the pollen was collected. In high doses, bees can suffer neurological damage from some insecticides, and in worst cases, they can be killed outright.

What if a colony contracts a disease? Should the beekeeper not control the problem, even if it may kill the colony and be transmitted to colonies located within foraging distance (1 to 3 miles, 1.6 to 4.8 kilometers) of the sick colony? It is imperative that all beekeepers be trained to detect symptoms of disease and pests to prevent the spread of these problems to other colonies. If a colony becomes diseased, it is very important that the beekeeper take measures to control the problem. However antibiotics and pesticides should be treatments of last resort because they interfere with the development of bees' natural defense mechanisms. Good beekeeping practices and cultural control measures should be the foundation of disease and pest control strategies. The second line of defense in maintaining bee health is the use and propagation of bee stocks that can defend themselves against diseases and parasites. More information on this is included throughout the book. Appendix A, page 114, provides detailed preventative measures for managing diseases and parasites. Appendix G, page 143, describes integrated pest management strategies for controlling these problems.

What Does the Future Hold?

The decline in honey bees mirrors the decline of other bee pollinators, but the plight of the honey bee has received more public attention. Will honey bees continue to decline, or will we be able change the trend in a more positive direction?

One fact that warrants some optimism is that humans and honey bees have enjoyed an intimate and mutual relationship throughout recorded history. People like honey and always have. Rock paintings depict honey hunters from ancient civilizations scaling cliff faces or tall trees to harvest honey from a bee nest. Bee trees in some parts of the world are protected and passed down as an inheritance within families. This tradition is still maintained, even in modern, mechanized North America. Many beekeepers today inherited their colonies and their bee lore from their parents and grandparents. Their great-grandparents brought honey bee colonies with them from the Old World because they couldn't leave them behind. This tradition will undoubtedly persist. There will always be beekeepers who keep bees (figure 2.6, page 20).

Another fact that weighs in favor of honey bees is that they are a superorganism, in all senses of the word. In terms of health, each individual bee has an immune system, which provides physiological defenses against diseases and parasites. But the

Umberto Moreno

Figure 2.6 A commercial beekeeper in North Dakota harvesting honey from his colonies. A fume board is placed over the hive boxes to drive the bees out of the upper boxes containing honey.

colony as a whole has collective behavioral defenses against pathogens and parasites, in addition to the individual physiological defenses. A strong colony with particular genetic traits can defend itself against a number of diseases and parasites in ways an individual bee cannot. This colony-level response of thousands of individual bees turns the female-based bee society into something more akin to a superheroine. The colony, when functioning as a large healthy organism, is awesome.

Strategy and Solutions

The best strategy for keeping bees healthy follows three deliberate steps: knowledge, prevention, and control. This sounds almost trite, but in fact most beekeepers jump from a little knowledge to a lot of control. Many go straight to the control step irrespective of knowledge. The strategy promoted here puts control last, and so requires human restraint and caution. It is easy for beekeepers to think they need to help the bees every step along the way. Despite our tendency to try to control nature, it is not healthy to fully domesticate bees, to make them reliant on us. Since the introduction of *Varroa* mites, we have made bees chemically dependent on our medications for their survival, and this is not a wise strategy. Bees really need to evolve their own defenses against dis-

eases and parasites. The best beekeepers follow the bees' lead, intervening to enhance the bees' natural tendencies, not to impede them or enslave them. The art of following their lead is the Prevention step of this strategy. Prevention is the missing link in many modern beekeeping practices.

In fact, the strategy outlined below applies to the management of all pollinators, not just honey bees. It is very important to heed the lessons we are learning about keeping honey bees healthy so we can manage alternative pollinators in an ecologically sustainable way.

1. Knowledge

- Learn about bee diseases and mite pests.
- Be able to recognize clinical symptoms of disease in your colony.
- Know the lifecycle of the mites.

2. Prevention

- Use good beekeeping practices to avoid getting and spreading diseases and mites.
- Bee self-defense! Use lines of bees that are resistant to diseases and mites.

3. Control

- Use cultural / mechanical / nonchemical control techniques to reduce transmission if your bees do have diseases or mites.
- Last resort: Use chemical treatments only when absolutely necessary.

Knowledge

Knowledge about honey bees is relatively easy to come by. There are a number of books and courses on good beekeeping practices that include information on recognizing bee diseases and the lifecycle of mites. The reader is encouraged to view the references at the end of this book (page 149) and to visit the on-line course on "Healthy Bees" that can be accessed through www.extension.umn.edu/honeybees. The best knowledge comes from reading and by being active in beekeeping associations. For every ten beekeepers there are ten "best" ways of keeping bees. But the best beekeepers think like a bee and are able to follow and artfully enhance the bee's lead.

Prevention

Beekeeping Practices

The most essential beekeeping practice is to make sure all colonies have large pollen and nectar stores at all times. Knowing when and how much to feed bees is an art and comes with experience. In general, the more proactive beekeepers are about providing supplemental feedings, the better. Good nutrition is critical for keeping healthy bees.

Another essential practice to prevent diseases is to replace all combs within the brood nest of every honey bee colony every three to five years. Traditionally, beekeepers do not replace combs because it is costly to replace the foundation, and it is energetically costly for the bees to secrete wax to build a new comb. Some beekeepers have beeswax combs that are over 30 years old.

Old combs in the brood nest can harbor disease spores from at least three honey bee diseases: American foulbrood (figure 2.7) caused by *Paenibacillus larvae*, chalkbrood (figure 2.8) caused by *Ascosphaera apis*, and nosema caused by *Nosema apis* (figure 2.9) and *N. ceranae*. These spores may remain viable in combs indefinitely. Many beekeepers have had the unfortunate experience of purchasing used equipment from a beekeeper, or hiving a new colony of bees in used equipment, and having the bees die from spores lurking in the combs.

Gary Reuter

Figure 2.8 Honey bee larvae affected by the fungal disease chalkbrood are hard and chalklike. These cadavers, or "mummies," here removed from cells, can be white or black in color depending on the spore production stage of the fungus.

Gary Reuter

Figure 2.9 A colony of honey bees during a long winter in Minnesota. Nosema is a gut parasite of adult bees that may cause the bees to defecate within the nest, which would contaminate the combs with disease spores. In this photo, the bees were able to fly out a short distance from the colony to defecate, but the amount of yellow snow indicates the colony is probably infected with Nosema.

In addition, beeswax absorbs some pesticides, depending on the properties of the particular compound. The accumulation of pesticides in beeswax most likely has negative effects on the health of bees.

Sampling

Sampling colonies for diseases and mites may be the most important thing a beekeeper can do. A little time spent on sampling could make or break a beekeeping operation. Colonies should be routinely sampled for *Varroa* mites and *Nosema*. Sampling tech-

Gary Reuter

Figure 2.7 American foulbrood, among the most destructive honey bee diseases, turns developing larvae into brown, smelly, and stringy goo.

niques can be found in beekeeping trade journals.

Sampling helps beekeepers make educated management and treatment decisions to control diseases and mites. If beekeepers assume that bees are healthy just because they look good, they may suddenly lose them three months later. If they assume that bees are diseased or infested with mites and they are treated without sampling, beekeepers may be spending a lot of time and money adding unnecessary and possibly harmful chemicals to colonies. Unnecessary treatments risk the contamination of wax and honey and lead to the eventual development of resistance to the treatment by the disease or mite. The old adage, "Better be safe than sorry" does not hold for unnecessary treatments!

Bee Self-Defense!

The wisest strategy for beekeepers is to keep bees that can defend themselves against diseases and mites. Honey bees can evolve resistance to pathogens and pests naturally over time, or they can be selectively bred for resistance. Keeping bees that can defend themselves allows beekeepers to reduce their reliance on chemical controls, which is the best solution in the long run.

One example of bees that have evolved natural resistance against *Varroa* mites is the subspecies of honey bees derived from Africa that were imported to Brazil in 1956. As they spread through South and Central America, Mexico, and the southern US, they became known as Africanized honey bees. Unfortunately, most colonies of Africanized bees have a personality that most beekeepers don't like: they are highly defensive. They are notorious for their ability to stage an impressive stinging attack when their nest is disturbed, making them impossible to keep in public areas and on farms where there are animals. They are not amenable to being transported en masse by truck for pollination, and so even if they are resistant to *Varroa* mites, they are not a viable alternative to our gentle European-derived honey bees. Could we selectively breed for a more gentle, Africanized bee that retains its resistance to mites? It's definitely worth a try.

Another bee that has evolved some natural resistance to *Varroa* mites is a line of bees derived from far eastern Russia, in the Primorsky Territory. These bees had been living with *Varroa* for many years. The USDA (Bee Research Lab in Baton Rouge, Louisiana) imported some of these bees in 1996. Some stock improvement has taken place in the US through field trials of the bees with commercial beekeepers, and Russian bees are now available commercially throughout the US. Many beekeepers like working with these bees and find they can reduce or eliminate the need for chemical treatments for both *Varroa* and tracheal mites, particularly when mite re-infestation from surrounding colonies (horizontal transmission) is not too high.

Bees already present in the US can be selectively bred for resistance. Two lines of bees have been bred and are commercially available: the MN Hygienic line, bred at the University of Minnesota, and the VSH (Varroa Sensitive Hygiene) line, bred at the USDA Bee Lab in Baton Rouge. Both lines are able to detect worker pupae that are infested with *Varroa* mites. Adult bees detect and remove the infested pupae from the cells and throw them out of the nest. The bees tend to detect that a pupa is infested with a mite after the mite has initiated oviposition (egg-laying). When the bees remove an infested pupa out of its cell, the reproductive cycle of the mite is interrupted, and any mite offspring are killed in the removal process. The net result is some pupae are sacrificed but the level of *Varroa* mites in the colony is reduced. The VSH line seems to specialize in detecting *Varroa* mites in worker pupae and removing the infested pupae. The MN Hygienic line has a more generalized response; in addition to removing mite-infested pupae, these bees also detect larvae and prepupae that are infected with American foulbrood and chalkbrood. The interesting thing is that hygienic bees detect diseased brood *before* the pathogen in the brood has reached the infectious stage. The bees remove the pathogen-infected brood from the cell and from the nest before it is contagious. Therefore, they do not risk transmitting the pathogen through the nest, and can curtail the progress of the disease through the colony entirely.

Any race or line of bees can be bred for hygienic behavior. For specific instructions see www.extension.umn.edu/honeybees. A beekeeper can get a head start on selecting for hygienic behavior simply by rearing queens from colonies that never show symptoms of chalkbrood.

In any breeding program it is absolutely essential to begin with a line of bees that produces honey, survives winter well, is gentle, and displays all the characteristics desired by the beekeeper. Do not select colonies for a single resistance trait without first evaluating their performance in other areas. The result will be colonies that express hygienic behavior or VSH, for example, but don't necessarily produce honey or survive the winter.

Here is an obvious question: If hygienic behavior is so good, why don't all honey bees in the US demonstrate this behavior? Why haven't they evolved this behavior on their own, in response to the challenge from diseases and *Varroa*? The answer lies with the queen-rearing industry in the US. The queen-rearing industry is a subsection of the beekeeping industry that rears and sells mated queen bees to other beekeepers nationwide. The genetics of our honey bee stocks in the US are controlled primarily by queen producers. The feral escapee colonies are basically non-existent in the US now due to *Varroa*, and the effects of natural selection are overpowered by man-assisted selection. Unfortunately, many queen producers still propagate and sell susceptible queens that cannot resist diseases and mites and so require chemical treatment.

The solution is for all beekeepers that raise queen bees, either for their own use or for sale, to propagate resistance traits. It is easy to select bees for hygienic behavior; that would be a good starting point. There are many fine lines of bees in the US, and it would be easy to select for hygienic behavior from among them. We would not lose genetic diversity this way. The drones (male bees) produced by colonies that demonstrate resistance would mate with queens bred for resistance, and it would be possible for all bees from many different lines and subspecies to express hygienic behavior.

One solution may be for the honey bee industry to implement stock certification programs. It is possible to certify that a particular line of bees is Russian, or displays hygienic or VSH behavior. A queen producer could command a good price for a certified queen. It is time to make this happen.

Control

Cultural / Mechanical / Nonchemical Control Techniques

Even with the most tenacious preventative measures, and even using lines of bees that demonstrate resistance, some colonies will come down with a disease, or the mite levels will increase to the point where treatment is needed or the colony will die. The chances that diseases and mites will spread in an operation will increase with the number colonies and frequency they are moved together on trucks and placed in common yards.

Before reaching for antibiotics and miticides, beekeepers should consider trying some alternative control tactics. For example, if a colony has American foulbrood, all the adult bees can be shaken off the combs that contain diseased brood and highly contagious spores, and the bees can be introduced into a new colony, on brand new combs. A new queen, one preferably bred for hygienic behavior, can be introduced into the new colony, and the colony can be fed sugar syrup until the disease spores the adult bees may be carrying are flushed through the system. By the time the new queen is laying eggs, the disease spores will be essentially eliminated, and the colony can continue on, disease free.

There are also methods that can be used to reduce mite levels. The best one is trapping the mites in drone brood. Because *Varroa* prefers to parasitize drone brood, a colony can be encouraged to rear drones by giving them combs with drone-sized brood cells. When the drones are pupating and full of mites, the combs can be removed from the colony and frozen until the drone pupae and mites die. If this process is repeated continuously over a summer, mite levels can be reduced considerably.

Good bee nutrition may serve both as a solid preventative and as a control. More research is needed on the link between good bee nutrition and resistance to diseases and parasites!

Chemical Controls

A goal in beekeeping should be to put chemical controls in last place, both in mind and in practice. Chemicals should only be used as a last resort, with great reluctance and restraint. Beekeepers should think, and think again, before applying antibiotics and miticides to bee colonies. There are now mite treatments based on the essential oil thymol or on organic acids such as formic and oxalic acid. They are relatively effective and if used properly will not lead to mite resistance nearly as fast as other pesticide treatments.

Knowledge. Prevention. Control. To keep bees healthy, spend the most time on the first two steps, which will enable you to eliminate or reduce the amount of time on the last step. Use control measures such as antibiotics and pesticides only as a last resort.

Why Keep Bees?

Honey bees, even with their problems, will always be the primary pollinator. The presence of a large variety of bees and flowers in our environment is hugely important to their mutual survival and ultimately, to our own. Having many bees in one area, whether social or solitary bees, ensures that many bees are foraging in a particular area. The more bees and more species of bees in our environment the better, particularly when there are many flowers within foraging range of the bees that require cross-pollination. Redirecting the downward trend in bee populations will involve awareness and change in our landscaping practices on many levels.

Beekeeping is considered a fringe hobby or occupation. Most people think beekeepers are eccentric. But beekeepers tend to have their feet firmly rooted in the earth and pay close attention to the environment; they function better out of doors than in the confines of a building. If more people would keep bees, any kind of bees, more people would become aware of surrounding flowers, insecticides, and ecology in general. Our environment needs more bees, flowers, and pollination. We need more win-win situations in the world. This book is a starting point.

3 A Brief Natural History of Bees

Marla Spivak, PhD, *Professor of Entomology, University of Minnesota*

What are bees? Bees are fuzzy flower-feeders with a sting. Bees look fuzzy because they have branched, or *plumose*, hairs (figure 3.1). These hairs help bees collect pollen from flowers. Bees and wasps are very close relatives and, understandably, many people confuse them. A little knowledge and careful inspection can help you readily tell them apart. Wasps do not have a fuzzy appearance, and they are carnivores (figure 3.2); their dietary source of protein comes from spiders, insects, and soft-bodied caterpillars and other larvae. The bees described in this book are all robust and fuzzy and quite distinct from the more shiny wasps.

Bees rarely bother people at picnics during late summer. Yellow jackets, one of many kinds of wasps, are the primary culprits. If you allow a yellow jacket to land momentarily on your sandwich, you will see it is shiny, not fuzzy. After that, you will rarely confuse bees and these wasps again. There are some flies that look like bees, but that confusion is also easily remedied. Flies only have two wings (figure 3.3, page 26). Bees and wasps have four wings, two on each side. You may see bees, wasps, and flies sucking nectar from flowers, as they all tap into this sweet sugar reward for a dietary source of carbohydrates. But only bees, with their fuzzy bodies, collect pollen from flowers.

Mace Vaughn

Figure 3.1
As the cost of honey bee pollination continues to rise, the services of other bee species, like this native melissodes bee, are more important than ever.

Cedar Creek Nature Center

Figure 3.2
Many wasps are predators of other insects. This baldfaced hornet has captured a dragonfly. Note the lack of pollen-collecting hairs.

Most people associate bees only with the bad experience of getting stung. However, the stinger is a remarkable feature with an interesting evolutionary history. Bees, wasps, and ants are classified together in an order of insects called the Hymenoptera (literally, "membranous wings") (figure 3.4, page 26). The

Figure 3.3
Not a bee! Some flies, such as this syrphid fly (*Mallota cimbiciform*), are hairy and have evolved to mimic bees as a way to discourage predators. Unlike bees, syrphid flies cannot sting.

most ancestral Hymenoptera are wasps, such as the modern-day sawflies (the Symphyta, which are not flies at all). The females in the oldest lineages of wasps have an *ovipositor*, or egg depositor, which injects their eggs into plant tissue. Some modern lineages use the ovipositor to place the egg into a spider or insect host. When the eggs hatch, the larvae feed on the plant tissue or on the host insect tissue. Over evolutionary time, the pointed ovipositor in the ancient wasps became modified into a stinger. Females of these wasps began to lay their eggs directly from the body. The sting and its associated venom in some present-day wasps enable females to paralyze their insect prey and then lay eggs on it. The sting also allows females of yet other wasp species and their relatives the ants to defend themselves and their developing offspring from predators. The sting, or even the threat of being stung, is an effective deterrent to large predators, including humans. Many people have an inordinate fear of bees, wasps, and ants. However, fear inspires curiosity, and if pursued, curiosity can lead to knowledge. Even a little knowledge about the importance of the bees, wasps, and ants to our environment can replace fear with perhaps a more reasonable response—healthy respect.

Over millennia, one lineage of stinging wasps led to present-day bees, which became vegetarians, relying on pollen and nectar from flowers for their protein and carbohydrates, respectively. Plumose hairs evolved, which helped trap the pollen grains on their bodies. These fuzzy, flower feeders with stingers, closely related to but modified from wasps, are called bees.

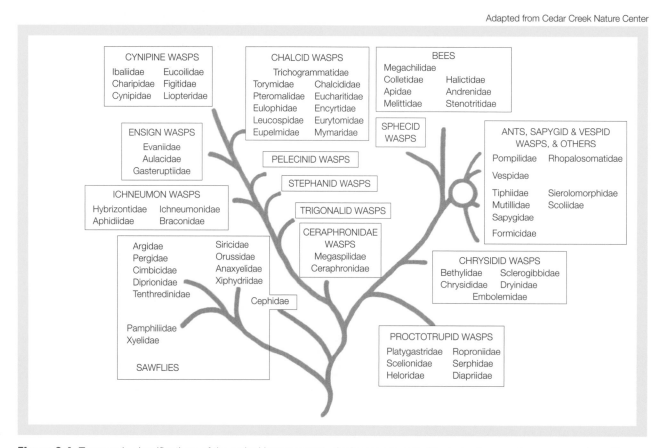

Figure 3.4 Taxonomic classifications of the order Hymenoptera—the insect group that includes bees, ants, wasps, and sawflies.

Bees

Bees and their most closely related wasps are grouped together in the superfamily Apoidea within the order Hymenoptera. The wasps within the Apoidea are called the Spheciformes (they are commonly referred to as sphecid wasps). The Apiformes, or bees, are thought to have arisen from a sphecid ancestor in the Early Cretaceous period of the Mesozoic era, approximately 100 million years ago. We know this because many bees collect resin from trees and have gotten trapped and fossilized within the resulting amber, which can be accurately dated.

Within the Apiformes, there are seven families of bees, which can be broadly grouped into two categories based on whether the tongue is relatively short or long. The short-tongued bee families are the Colletidae, Andrenidae, Stenotritidae, Halictidae, and the Melittidae. The long-tongued bee families include the Megachilidae and the Apidae. The bee pollinators discussed in this book are Halictidae (alkali bees), Megachilidae (mason bees, leafcutter bees (figure 3.5), and Apidae (bumble bees and honey bees)— one short-tongued and two long-tongued families.

Grouping organisms based on tongue length may seem ludicrous, but it is a critical distinguishing characteristic among bees. A bee's tongue is an intricate apparatus, made up of segmented parts and palps that fold up neatly under the bee's "chin" when not in use. Bees with long tongues have modified palps that, when extended, form a sheath around a central segmented structure called a glossa, resulting in a type of sucking straw to help draw in nectar from tubular flowers. The palps in short-tongued bees do not form a long sheath, and these bees prefer drinking nectar from shallow cup-shaped flowers. In general, the length of the tongue reflects the types of flowers the bees visit for food, kind of like having the right tool for the job.

Contrary to many organisms, the greatest diversity of bee species is found in arid and semiarid regions of the world, not in the tropics. In the US, the greatest number of bee species can be found in the deserts of the Southwest. They are also abundant in deserts of Chile and Argentina, more southern (temperate) parts of Australia, Southern Africa, Central Asia, and the Mediterranean. You do not need to travel to exotic locations, however, to find a vast number of bee species. Simply walk out to the backyard. Many people claim they haven't seen bees on their flowers in years, but if we would stop buzzing about and sit still for 30 quiet minutes in the garden on a sunny day, bees will appear seemingly out of thin air. Bees are out there, particularly on native floral species. If we stand still, they will come to us.

Social and Solitary Bees

It is a curious fact that some insects tolerate living in close proximity to each other, often within a single nest. Within the order Hymenoptera, some species of wasps and bees, and all species of ants, evolved social behaviors, living in colonies and interacting in complex and sophisticated ways. However, most species of wasps and bees live strictly solitary lives (figure 3.6, page 28). Some solitary bees and wasps aggregate their individual nests in one location, splitting the difference between going it entirely alone and having nest-mates.

Honey bees are probably the most well known of the social bees because they produce honey and have made headlines with Colony Collapse Disorder. Most people recognize bumble bees as they fly from flower to flower, but few people appreciate that they

Ralph Holzenthal

body hairs branched or plumose

FEMALE

scopa (pollen basket) on abdomen

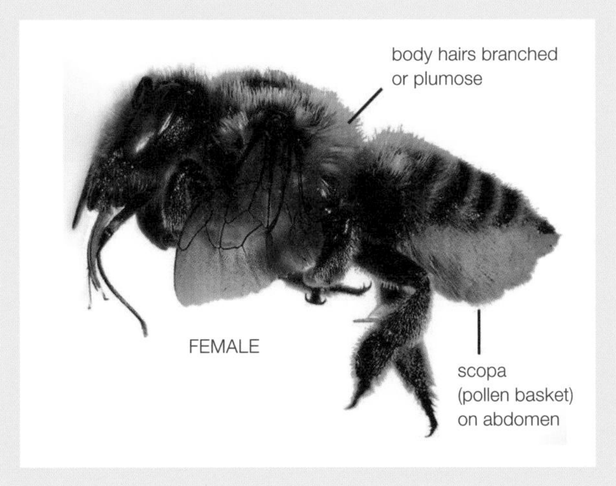

Figure 3.5 The family Megachilidae includes the solitary cavity-nesting leafcutter and mason bees, like this *Megachile latimanus*, a native leafcutter bee species. Unlike honey bees and bumble bees, which carry pollen on specially adapted hind legs, the megachilids carry pollen on stiff hairs located on the underside of their abdomen, called the scopa.

Ralph Holzenthal

Figure 3.6 The majority of the world's bees are solitary species that nest below ground, such as this metallic green *Halictus sericeus*, a native of the Midwest.

also are social. A honey bee colony is perennial; the queen and her workers live together year-round and survive together through hot summers and cold winters (figure 3.7). In contrast, a bumble bee society is annual; the size of the group alternates between a single queen who hibernates underground during the winter months and a colony of individuals who live together in a nest during the summer. A honey bee colony is like a perennial tree; a bumble bee colony is more like an annual plant that begins from seed each year.

Three other bees described in this book— mason, leafcutter, and alkali bees—are solitary. Each female constructs her own nest and provides food for her offspring. Some females may aggregate their individual nests in a particular location, but they do not interact or help each other. In fact, the egg-laying female does not live long enough to see her offspring complete development; she dies leaving her legacy behind.

Why do some bees prefer to interact with each other while others can't tolerate it? Why do only some bees live in a group? Apparently, it works just fine for most insects and most species of bees and wasps to go it alone. In the case of bees, however, they are successful and abundant when they have access to a diverse array of floral resources and ample places to lay their eggs. When these resources are limited, their populations may decline. Living in a group must be advantageous, especially in these limiting environmental conditions, or they wouldn't do it. In fact, some bee species in the family Halictidae can be solitary in one environment and social in another. This gives us a clue that environment must have played a role in the early stages of social behavior. Way back when, if it was difficult for bees to find nesting sites—for example, hollow twigs or cavities or soil of the right consistency for digging a hole— some bees might have grouped together where these resources were adequate, thus increasing chances for survival. Also, if floral resources were patchy or scarce, it may have been helpful for populations of individuals to cluster where resources were rich. With a sting as a defense, a female could remain close to her developing offspring and defend them from predators or even from members of the same species that might want to stage a takeover of an already provisioned nest. These scenarios may help explain why some bees tolerate living in close proximity, and why they would be gregarious.

The next puzzle about group living is why members within the group would forego mating and reproduction, allowing one or a few females to reap the direct genetic benefits of laying all the eggs. Wouldn't it make sense biologically for each female to have her own genetic offspring? Most scientists agree that for true colony life to evolve, for insects to interact within a nest and allow only one or more of the females to lay eggs, the group members within the nest must be related to some degree. If they aren't initially related, in time they may come to

Kate Ihle

Figure 3.7 A honey bee queen (center) surrounded by her attendants.

28 Managing Alternative Pollinators

share genes if one or a few females become the primary egg-layer(s). Sharing a majority of genes provides a sort of glue to hold the interests of the group together. What are the interests of the group? They are long-term—very, very long-term. To be successful, members of the group must have their characteristics (genes and how these genes play out as traits in particular environments) propagated in subsequent generations, for millennia to come. If they can't reproduce directly by laying their own eggs, they can reproduce indirectly by helping their mother and sisters lay eggs. If more individuals of common descent can be produced in the long run by the counter-intuitive strategy of foregoing immediate personal reproduction, then long-term interests automatically kick in and persist as inclusive fitness benefits.

It is hard for humans to think about very long-term, evolutionary costs and benefits. For all the thinking we do, we tend to prefer thinking of short-term, more immediate benefits. Fortunately, insects don't think the way we do. They respond to the environment and to each other, they learn simple and even complex things, but they do not think about thinking. This may be one reason for their very long-term success.

Within a social colony of insects, even with their shared long-term reproductive interests and overall cooperation, there is still conflict among individuals. This give-and-take among individuals, even among relatives, seems to be the crux of life. Cooperation and conflict is evident in all living things, from bacteria to elephants, so it is no surprise that life isn't always peaceful in insect societies. There are always a few cheaters and thieves. There are always females that sneak in their own eggs when the primary egg-layer is not aware, or even at certain predictable times of year in full sight of the queen, as in some bumble bee colonies. How social insects balance conflict and cooperation is a fruitful and relevant area of study.

Honey bee and bumble bee societies, although different from each other, are rich and complex. They are female-based societies with no central authority. This fact comes as a surprise to many people: How can a society survive without a ruler? We call the egg-laying female a queen but she is not an authoritative figure. She has the privilege of mating and laying fertilized eggs, and so of directly propagating her genes, but she does not rule the roost, she does not bark out orders. Who rules? The short answer is all individuals in the nest rule themselves. They organize themselves based on innate behavioral patterns and information gleaned from interactions with nest mates and the environment. The society is self-organized as a complex, interactive network—as an emergent property. The individuals within the society constitute one level of organization, and the colony constitutes another level of organization, often quite different than the sum of the parts. The building blocks of the social colony are the behaviors of individual bees, but when the individuals come together, colony-level behaviors emerge. A honey bee colony can be considered as an organism, or superorganism, and many colonies in a landscape can be considered a community. Social insects are fascinating because they stretch the human mind to think outside our social and political spheres. They force us to learn something from very ancient and successful types of societies. They force us to consider their solitary origins. This is one reason, among many, to respect and protect bees, both solitary and social.

Development and Reproduction of Bees

It is useful here to review how an individual insect such as a solitary bee develops from egg to adult. An assembly of developing individuals in one nest can form one level of organization that eventually may evolve into a society at yet another level of organization, bringing us full circle.

Most organisms, including humans, simply grow. In contrast, some insects transform from one body type to another as they grow. This transformation, or metamorphosis, is an amazing feat. Bees undergo a complete metamorphosis, as they progress through four developmental stages: egg, larva, pupa, and adult. The most remarkable transformations occur during the pupal stage when the cells, tissues, and organs that were necessary for the larva to function are reorganized and remodeled to accommodate the functions of the future adult.

An adult female bee lays an egg (figure 3.8, page 30), which is white and elongated with a soft membrane around it. The egg is laid directly on the nest substrate or on a mass of pollen that was provisioned by an adult bee.

Figure 3.8
Bees hatch from eggs laid by their mother. These white honey bee eggs are smaller than a grain of rice.

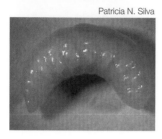

Figure 3.9
During their larval stage, bees are white grubs, as this fifth instar honey bee, that do not resemble their adult form.

The egg changes into a larva, a soft white grub with no legs (figure 3.9). The larva is an eating machine. If the egg was laid on a mass of pollen, the larva is said to have been mass provisioned by the mother, and will spend its larval phase of life engorging itself on the pollen. If the larva was laid directly on the substrate, it will be progressively provisioned, or fed frequently by adult bees. Most bee larvae are mass provisioned. Progressive provisioning of larvae occurs in some species of bumble bee and in all honey bees. In all cases, as the larva eats it must shed its cuticle, or molt, to grow. Honey bee larvae, for example, go through five molts. The larval stages between molts are called instars, so a honey bee larva is said to have five instars. Bumble bees, mason bees, leafcutter bees, and alkalai bees have four or five instars, depending on the species.

At the end of the last larval instar, the larva will stop eating and will defecate for the first time. This sounds like an extraneous fact, but it is an important one. Bee larvae spend their instars resting on the food that is provided or fed to them, and it is important not to contaminate that food with waste. It is an incredible adaptation that in young larvae, there is no connection between the mid and hind gut until the last larval instar.

After defecating, the larva is called a prepupa. In some bee species, the prepupa is the stage that survives the winter, or remains for long periods of time, sometimes over a year, before completing development. Remaining in suspended development is a strategy for timing the rest of development to coincide with floral blooms so the adult does not emerge during a dearth or cold weather.

At some point, either right after defecating or after a period of suspended development, the prepupa of most bee species produces silk from glands located near the mouth and will spin a thin but strong silk cocoon around itself. The silk is secreted from the glands as a liquid, but upon contact with air, solidifies into fine fibers. Within this protected cocoon, the bee, now called a pupa (figure 3.10) begins the process of reorganization and development of cells, tissues, and organs to transform into the adult body. In bees, the pupal stage proceeds relatively quickly. Bees do not survive winter or long periods of time as pupae. For example, the pupal stage of female (worker) honey bees is about 12 to 13 days. When the pupa has completed its development, an adult bee emerges, or ecloses, from the cocoon.

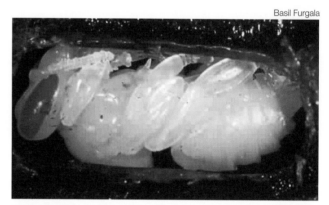

Figure 3.10 As a pupa, the immature bee looks like a white adult. The eyes are usually the first part of the body to develop pigmentation.

Haplodiploidy

Which sex will eclose from the pupa, an adult male or female? In the order Hymenoptera, the female wasps, ants, and bees are produced from fertilized eggs, and the males are produced from unfertilized eggs. When an egg is fertilized by a sperm, two sets of chromosomes combine (one set from the mother, the other from the father) to produce a *diploid* individual. If the egg is not fertilized, the haploid egg containing a single set of chromosomes will develop into a male. This means the males are haploid, and the females are diploid—a condition called haplodiploidy (see sidebar, below).

The males look entirely normal, but they only inherit one set of genetic instructions solely from the mother. The main function of the males is to mate, so in one sense they are merely flying female gametes. They have a grandfather but no father. Haploid males seem like a perplexing trick of nature from the human perspective.

Adult bees have short or long life spans, depending on the species. In most bee species, the first thing the new adults do is fly off to forage and mate. Males will usually die soon after mating. The haploid set of genetic instructions in each male provides just enough guidance to enable him to nourish himself on flowers, locate a female of the same species, pass on his genes, and die; short and sweet. Females on the other hand have a number of options. For some species, after the female mates, she and her supply of stored sperm may enter hibernation, or diapause, for a variable amount of time, often until the next year. The following spring or summer, she will emerge from diapause, find a nest site, collect pollen, and deposit fertilized and unfertilized eggs in the nest for the next generation. After provisioning the nest, the female may leave it and die, as do the leafcutter and mason bees described in this book. In bumble bees, a queen emerges in late summer, mates, and enters diapause for the winter. In spring, she will emerge, find, and provision a new nest. She will remain with her offspring in a social setting, laying eggs until late in the summer when she will die after producing a new batch of daughter queens. In honey bees, mated queens return to the natal nest without ever entering diapause and spend their entire lives in a populous society, laying thousands of eggs almost slavishly.

How and where bees mate is a great topic for cocktail party conversation. After males eclose as adults, they may spend their days cruising around flowers where females of the same species will also forage for food. The males then pounce on a female right there in an aromatic floral cafeteria. Alternatively, males may cruise nest entrances, particularly when the nests are aggregated in the same area, waiting for a female to depart on her first flight. This may seem like an overly direct way of passing on one's genes, but it is very efficient. Finally, males and females may meet on non-floral vegetation or in the sky, finding each other by cueing into common features of the landscape or other celestial cues, or by unique odors produced by the bees.

The honey bee mating story is worth even more detail. A 5 to 7 day-old virgin queen leaves her nest

DIPLOID MALES AND INBREEDING

Male production in *haplodiploid* species can be complex—in some situations, diploid males can be formed. Diploid males occur when there is inbreeding in a population, with the result that a chromosome from the mother and one from the father have the exact genetic information in a critical place. The sameness cancels out the diploid state at that particular genetic location, or *sex-determining locus*, and the genetic instructions are only translated as if they came from a single, haploid chromosome.

Diploid males are generally useless; depending on the species, they are either killed by the females or do not propagate themselves. Inbreeding and resulting diploid male production might occur when there is severe disturbance in the environment such that only small, local populations of bees remain that must mate among relatives. The worst case scenario is that the local inbred population may become extinct (Zayed and Packer, 2005).

It is extremely important to preserve enough natural habitats for bees so they can flourish and avoid mating with relatives. Our job is to be good stewards of our environment, which will allow bees to avoid the threat of inbreeding and production of diploid males on their own.

and is smart enough to circle around it several times, taking mental snapshots of where her nest is located, so she can find it again upon her return from her eventful day. Without prior knowledge or instruction as to where she should fly, she locates a *drone congregation area* where males from many neighboring colonies are flying in circles 20 to 30 feet (~6 to 9 meters) in the air. To this day, the cues the females and males use to find these areas remain a mystery. Every afternoon in the summer months, when temperatures are warm and skies are clear, the males approach the entrance of the nest, check out the weather, groom themselves, and then fly out to meet other males in these congregation areas. They return to the nest a time or two to tank up on honey to fuel another 20 to 30 minutes of cruising before calling it a day. If they are lucky, they will encounter a virgin female and pass on their genes before dying. If they do not mate, at least they pass their afternoons trying. The female honey bee does not stop mating after encountering one male. She mates with 10 to 20 males, sometimes more, within one hour before returning to the nest. She may take another mating flight on a subsequent day if she did not encounter sufficient drones the first day. After mating, her behaviors change, and she will not fly out to mate again. She stores a portion of each male's sperm in a receptacle, called a *spermatheca*, in her abdomen for the remainder of her life. As eggs mature in her ovaries and pass down one by one through the oviduct, she can release sperm (or not) from her spermatheca to fertilize eggs (or not). This is an excellent example of planned parenthood, with no political ramifications.

The females in most bumble bee species mate once. Females and males find each other in the air, fall to the ground, and remain in copula for hours. Leafcutter and mason bees quickly mate with one or more males at the nest site and get on with things.

Full Circle: Solitary and Social Bees

A solitary bee, such as a leafcutter bee, mason bee, or alkali bee, begins life as a larva eating a mass of pollen provided by the mother, who the bee will never meet. The larva is not completely alone; he or she shares a nest (hollow twig or soil tunnel) with developing brothers and sisters. They each develop in separate compartments within the nest that the mother partitioned off using leaves or mud. There may be many nests aggregated in one area, a feature that can be exploited to manage these bees as pollinators. After consuming the larva's share of pollen, the developing bee will enter diapause, passing through the rest of summer, fall, and winter as a prepupa in a state of suspended animation, and complete the pupal development rapidly the following spring. In some cases, the bee may complete development to the adult stage the same year. In either case, after eclosing as an adult, the bee mates right away, ideally with individuals from a different nest. The male dies soon after mating, and the female then does the environment an invaluable service of collecting pollen from the flowers that are blooming around her. She uses the pollen to provision her own nest as the mother of the next generation. She has no help from other bees, and will die before her offspring complete their development the next year. These pollinating bees should be celebrated upon their emergence every spring or summer; the rest of the year they are dormant and quiet to the world.

A female bumble bee spends all or part of her life in company of her mother and sisters. A mated female bumble bee lays eggs on pollen but does not abandon her offspring. She stays put on the nest, caring for her offspring. She incubates them, defends them from predators, collects pollen and nectar for them, and secretes wax to construct and enlarge the nest. When daughters complete development and are adults, the colony becomes social: mother and daughters interact on the nest; the daughters cooperate in brood care, nest provisioning, and defense; and there is reproductive division of labor—the mother lays eggs, and at least for a while, the workers do not. Later in the season as the colony grows, the emerging daughters seem to act like rebellious human teenagers, and begin to challenge the mother's role as egg-layer. They may start laying their own unfertilized, male-destined eggs and compete with their mother. Eventually, the mother loses reproductive control of the nest and dies. The large daughters produced last in the colony life cycle fly off, mate, and spend the winter underground. In spring they emerge from the ground to begin a nest, only to experience the same rebellion from their own daughters in a few short months.

A honey bee colony shows no remnants of its solitary origins. No individual in the nest can live on its own for an extended time. They are all dependent on each other for survival and reproduction: the queen cannot feed herself or find her own nest, and the daughters can never fly off and mate. The individuals have distinctive and important roles in the nest, but they are nothing without each other. The colony is the organism, a super-organism that contains thousands of organisms within it, and each organism contains organelles made up of organic materials, which can be reduced ad infinitum to smaller and smaller units. When a beekeeper maintains thousands of honey bee colonies for pollination, the super-organisms interact as populations. Each level of organization is dependent on its interaction with the environment for survival; that environment ranges from the internal physiology and nutrition of one individual to climatic patterns of the globe.

Figure 3.11
Face-to-face with a worker honey bee. Even the eyes are covered with hairs.

Bees, whether solitary or social, are great portals to the environment. Humans who have become disconnected from nature could readily find their bearings by paying attention to bees and the flowers they feed on. The seasonal cycle of a solitary or social bee can be followed with minimal effort, resulting in heightened appreciation and respect for nature and the environment from a bee's perspective. When you view the world through the multi-faceted eyes of a bee (figure 3.11), you can never go back; it is a marvelous place.

4 Pollination Botany

Eric Mader, *Pollinator Outreach Coordinator, the Xerces Society for Invertebrate Conservation*
Marla Spivak, PhD, *Professor of Entomology, University of Minnesota*

A flower is nothing more than a short modified branch. Flower petals are nothing more than modified leaves. And yet for the farmer and beekeeper—or anyone who likes to eat—life depends upon the development of this structure (figure 4.1).

Flowers are the reproductive apparatus that allow genetic exchange between two parent plants. The offspring that result are a new combination of inherited characteristics, with new instructions for life. Some of these offspring will have an enhanced ability to survive. Some will not.

The botanical details of pollination outlined in this section may seem confusing at first, but an understanding of flower characteristics can be extremely valuable when one is confronted with the challenge of pollinating a new or unusual crop. With a little knowledge, flowers can be seen from a pollinator's point of view. For example, the flat surface of some flowers provide a safe landing place for insects that rest while feeding, such as flies, butterflies, and beetles. Simple tubular flowers are more attractive to animals that hover while feeding, such as hummingbirds and some moths.

Flower Parts and their Functions

As with animals, the individual male and female sex cells contained within flowers are called gametes. The male gamete is contained within small granular storage structures called pollen. Pollen is produced at the end of a slender stalk, or filament, on a structure called an anther. Together anther and filament form the male component of the flower, or stamen.

The female component, or pistil, consists of three parts: an *ovary*—usually at the base of the flower—from which arises a stalk called the *style*, bearing a sticky landing pad called a *stigma* to which pollen adheres.

The ovary of a flower contains one or more unfertilized ovules. Upon fertilization an ovule joins with sperm to form a single cell called the zygote. The entire structure of the flower is adapted with this process as the goal. As this zygote grows, it divides into a multicelled structure that we recognize as a seed. In some plants, ovary walls, called the pericarp, enlarge to form a fruit containing the seeds. These fruits may be soft and fleshy like an apple, or dry and hard like a walnut. Whatever its form, without fertilization, fruit will not develop. In fruits that contain multiple seeds, all ovules must be fertilized for the fruit to reach its maximum size.

In addition to the structures listed above, a flower may have other parts. Some of these include a series of short green leaves, called *sepals*, which form a protective *calyx* around an unopened flower bud. The

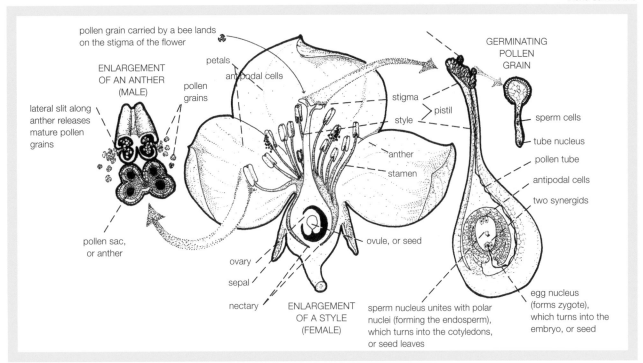

Figure 4.1 Fertilization of a flower.

petals, or *corolla*, together with the sepals, form the flower's *perianth*. The entire flowering structure is borne on the receptacle of the *pedicel*, or flower stalk.

It is worth noting that while all plants reproduce, not all plants flower. Primitive plants such as mosses and ferns produce spores in a reproductive process similar to that of fungi.

Flower Types

There are tremendous variations in flowers between plants of different species, and various ways of categorizing plants based on flower characteristics. Among the most basic classification is separation based on the number of flower parts. Monocotyledons (including grasses, orchids, lilies, and palms) consist of flower parts (such as stamens or petals) in groups of three. Dicotyledons (such as most broadleaf plants) contain flower parts in groups of four or five. Flowers containing only the bare minimum number of parts (as opposed to some multiple of the basic number), are called simple flowers.

A second way to categorize flowers is based on the presence or absence of typical flower structures.

Tulips for example lack the protective green sepals found on other flowers, and instead have modified green leaves that slowly change color to resemble petals. These *tepals* are in fact neither flower nor petal, and hence tulips are described as an *incomplete*, as opposed to a *complete, flower*.

Flowers that contain both male and female reproductive parts—stamen and pistil—are sometimes called perfect flowers. Flowers bearing only the male or female parts are called imperfect. In addition, some plants will bear both separate male and female flowers (such as squash), or flowers with both male and female parts (such as apple) on a single plant. These are called monoecious. Other plants (including willow, holly, and sumac) have female and male flowers on separate plants. These are called dioecious, and plants with both flower types are needed for pollination to occur.

Finally, flowers may occur individually or as clusters of multiple flowers called an inflorescence. Sometimes the flowers of an inflorescence will be fused into a single structure that is sometimes mistaken for a single flower. Sunflowers, coneflowers (figure 4.2, page 36), and dandelions are classic examples

Figure 4.2 Composite flowers like this purple coneflower (*Echinacea purpurea*) may look like a single structure, but are actually composed of many small, tightly packed flowers.

Figure 4.5 The highly branched flowers of this Joe-Pye weed (*Eupatorium purpureum*) form a panicle, which is being visited by a leafcutter bee.

of this—a single sunflower head, called a composite flower, is made up of hundreds of individual flowers.

Other inflorecences include the *spike* with multiple flowers fused directly to a single stalk without individual stems. The flowers of *Liatris* (figure 4.3), yucca, and Culver's root are all examples of spike inflorescences. The raceme is an inflorescence with flowers attached to a single stalk via short stems, such as bellflower (figure 4.4), foxglove, penstemon, and delphinium. A panicle is a raceme in which the individual flower stems are compoundly branched, like Joe-Pye weed (figure 4.5), hydrangea, and crape myrtle blossoms. Finally an umbel consists of multiple flower stems arising from a single point on the tip of a stalk. Common umbelliferous flowers include Golden Alexanders (figure 4.6), carrot, dill, and yarrow.

Figure 4.3 Tall blazing star (*Liatris aspera*) has a spike-type inflorescence with the flowers attached directly to the main stem.

Figure 4.4 A raceme is a type of inflorescence with the flowers attached to the main stem by a short stalk, such as this creeping bellflower (*Campanula rapunculoides*).

Figure 4.6 An umbel is a type of inflorescence in which the flower stalks originate at one point on the tip of the stem, such as with this Golden Alexander (*Zizia aurea*). Such flowers are often highly attractive to flies.

Flower Reproduction

Despite the tremendous energy that plants put into flowering, reproduction really only begins when a pollen grain comes to rest on a flower's stigma. If the pollen grain is compatible with the host flower, then pollen germination begins. In the case of many plants, the gametes are self-incompatible, meaning that the pollen must come from another plant.

Each individual grain of pollen consists of two cells. After transfer, one of these cells elongates, forming a long microscopic tube that penetrates down through the length of the style, growing closer to the ovules located at the base of the pistil. Elongation of this pollen tube is rapid, and is fueled by nutrients and hormones supplied by the pistil.

Eventually the pollen tube enters a tiny pore in the ovule which terminates at an unfertilized egg. While one cell of the pollen grain forms this pollen tube, the second cell divides to form two sperm cells. The first of these sperm cells travels down the pollen tube, completing fertilization of the waiting egg, and forming the zygote. The second sperm cell also travels down the pollen tube and combines with another cell in the ovule to form a food storage tissue called endosperm. Together the zygote and endosperm form the embryo—a miniature plant. As the embryo matures, it remains enclosed in the ovary, which slowly enlarges to form the completed seed.

When pollen is not transferred to the receptive stigma, no seed is formed. Many flowers, such as apples, may contain multiple ovules. If only a little pollen is transferred between flowers, not all of the eggs may become fertilized. The result is fewer seeds with correspondingly smaller fruit. These problems can occur when pollination vectors, such as bees, are absent.

Pollination by Wind and Animals

Many of our most common plant species, including grasses, conifers, and food plants such as wheat, rice, and corn (figure 4.7), are wind pollinated.

Physical movement of pollen via wind, which evolved before insects, requires less energy and results in small, inconspicuous flowers. But wind pollination also has limitations: Most of the copious amounts of pollen produced by these plants does not

Eric Mader

Figure 4.7 Wind-pollinated plants like corn produce a lot of pollen but lack the showy, colorful appearance of animal-pollinated plants.

reach a compatible ovule. Wind speed and direction are unpredictable. Wind-pollinated plants usually need to grow in dense stands of the same species.

Early insects consumed some of this windblown pollen, and over millions of years those insects evolved into the bees and other pollinators that exist today. Plants adapted along with these pollinators, resulting in large showy flowers that are now entirely dependent on animal pollination (figure 4.8).

Eric Mader

Figure 4.8 The red color, abundant nectar, and deep tubular flowers of this cardinal flower (*Lobelia cardinalis*) make it a hummingbird favorite.

The beauty of these flowers does not exist for people, but rather for the creatures that visit them. Flowers are advertising. Colored petals provide contrast against green foliage and offer a landing platform for insects to rest while feeding. Scents, whether pleasant or putrid, attract the chemical sensors of insect antennae. Plants may provide excess pollen (which is high in protein) for insects to eat. To encourage additional visitation, a carbohydrate fuel, nectar, is often provided to power the exhausting flights made by pollinating bees, butterflies, and hummingbirds.

Some flowers provide small droplets of nectar that may be readily available for inefficient pollinators like flies. Flowers that do this, such as fennel, are sometimes called low-reward flowers. High-reward flowers, on the other hand, may provide copious amounts of nectar hidden deep within the inner recesses, where only the largest, most efficient pollinators can reach them.

A classic example of a high-reward flower is bottle gentian (*Gentiana andrewsii*), a native prairie plant of North America (figure 4.9). The petals of bottle gentian are closed at the top hiding the reproductive parts within. It attracts large muscular bumble bees

Eric Mader

Figure 4.9 Bottle gentian (*Gentiana andrewsii*) is an unusual flower with petals that remain closed. The plant is entirely dependent on bumble bees—which are strong enough to force their way inside—for pollination.

which are able to manipulate the petals and push their way inside the flower where they are rewarded with large quantities of nectar.

The color patterns of flowers often provide additional cues to passing insects about the quality and quantity of a flower's nectar. Many flowers feature ultraviolet nectar guides which are only visible to bees. However the nectar is offered, visitors are forced to brush against anther and stigma to find it.

The result of all this effort is more direct and reliable pollination for the plant without having to rely on the uncertainties of wind. For their part, animal pollinators are often extremely loyal to their host plants during the bloom period. A bee, for example, will often fly from the same species flower to another in succession, ignoring other blooming plants along the way. This loyalty can reach evolutionary extremes where both plant and pollinator become so specialized that each is entirely dependent on the other. This specialization is risky with extinction of the pollinator resulting in the extinction of the plant, and vise versa. The example of bottle gentian mentioned previously is illustrative: in many areas of its range the plant is now rare both due to habitat loss for the plant and the disappearance of its pollinators.

Specialization of this sort is rare, and just as plants and pollinators can become increasingly dependent upon each other, they can also grow apart. In fact some plants have developed emergency back-up plans for survival, such as self-fertility, when insect pollinators are scarce. Thus plants like soybeans, whose flowers have all the classic adaptations of insect pollination, can set seed with nary a bee in sight. In these types of plants the stamen may grow into a long curved arc which eventually contacts its own stigma. Similarly, pollen-hungry bees sometimes forage from a wind-pollinated species like sweet corn.

Just as extreme specialization is the exception, so too are extreme divergences. For even with self-pollinated flowers, seed production is often greater with insect visitation. And while plants like corn may produce vast clouds of pollen, the individual grains are small, low in nutrition, and spoil easily compared to insect-pollinated plants. The general trend for both plant and pollinator is a need for diversity. Animal pollinators need a diverse selection and succession of flo-

ral food sources to survive. Plants prosper by adapting to predation, disease, and changing environmental conditions. These adaptations only occur through the genetic diversity inherent in cross-pollination. Without the other, neither plant nor pollinator can exist.

Determining Optimal Pollinator by Flower Type

The various traits a flower exhibits are called pollinator syndromes by botanists (table 4.1, page 42). These traits include a flower's size, shape, color, scent, amount of nectar and pollen, and the time of day in which a flower blooms. Variations in any of these traits make a flower more or less appealing to specific types of pollinators.

By understanding the typical characteristics of different pollinator syndromes, you can make an educated guess as to what animal may visit a particular flower (figure 4.10). In fact, even completely unrelated plants may have similar looking flowers if they are visited by the same species of bee. This type of knowledge can be valuable when faced with the challenge of propagating an unusual plant species for which little published information exists.

It is important to remember that pollination syndromes are not static. Rather, the traits that flowers exhibit are in a state of continuous change as both flower and pollinator adapt to take better advantage of each other.

Diverse Bees, Diverse Flowers

There are many species of bees. They come in various sizes with various tongue lengths. All bees are attracted to similar colors and aromas of flowers. Some flowers have long and narrow *corollas,* and the nectar can only be reached by a very long-tongued bee such as a bumble bee. For example, the nectar in red clover blossoms is readily accessible to bumble bees but not to other bees with shorter tongues.

Smaller bees, such as honey bees and leafcutter bees, may be allured by the smell of red clover but may have a hard time reaching the nectar and pollen with their tongues. So, they will switch foraging preference to dutch or sweet clover, with more open petals and easier-to-reach rewards.

Figure 4.10 Legumes, such as this showy tick trefoil (*Desmodium canadense*), often have asymmetrical flower petals with an extended stamen column. The unusual shape of the petals directs bees toward the nectar reward. The reproductive structures are adapted to the way bees approach the flower.

Similarly, the flowers of blueberry plants also have a long corolla that proves difficult for a honey bee. A smaller bee may be able to sneak the whole body inside the flower and enjoy the pollen and nectar at the base of the tubular corolla. A bumble bee can reach the rewards with her long tongue from outside the flower. But this floral shape is difficult for honey bees to visit effectively.

Other flowers, particularly in the family Solenaceae, which includes tomatoes, eggplants, and peppers, do not release pollen from the anther unless the anther is sonicated, or vibrated very quickly. Bumble bees specialize in sonicating, or buzz pollination, of tomato flowers. They grab the flower in their mandibles and vibrate their flight muscles, releasing the pollen. Honey bees, leafcutter bees, and mason bees are not able to buzz-pollinate so you will rarely, if ever, see these bees on tomatoes.

Alfalfa is another interesting example of an unusual flower. Alfalfa flowers resemble other legumes with one large upper petal, two side petals, and two fused bottom keel petals. Those two keel petals hold an unusual surprise however. Together they hold the stamen under tension. When a probing insect steps on those petals, the stamen is released, and it springs forward slamming into the upper petal (figure 4.11). This process insures that a visiting bee is dusted with pollen. Some bees, including honey bees, dislike being wacked on the head repeatedly and learn to avoid alfalfa flowers when easier forage sources are nearby.

One final point is that bee pollinators are often extremely loyal to their host plants during the bloom period. A bee, for example, will often fly from the same species flower to another in succession, ignoring other blooming plants along the way. This loyalty ensures the plant will be pollinated. On another day or at another time, a bee may switch her preference to another species of flower, but again will stay loyal to that flower over multiple visits.

Pollination and Bee Nutrition

Bees are oblivious to the huge pollination service they perform. Pollen is bees' sole dietary source of protein. They absolutely require pollen from a variety of plants to feed to their offspring (larvae). The protein level in pollen from different plant sources ranges from 2.5 to 60 percent, and bees prefer pollens with high protein levels. Pollen also contains some lipids, sterols, vitamins, minerals, and carbohydrates.

Wind-pollinated plants like corn, which span thousands of acres across the US, produce lots of pollen. But corn pollen to bees is somewhat equivalent to corn cobs to humans: bland fiber. If starved, or if

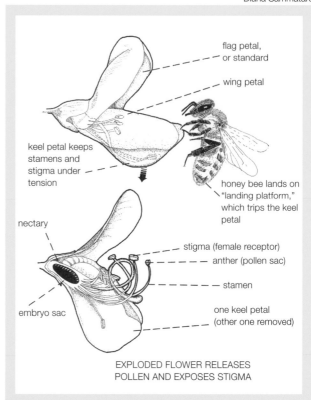

Diana Sammataro

Figure 4.11 A honey bee tripping an alfalfa flower.

corn pollen is the only source of protein around, bees will collect it. Grass pollen, like corn, is of low nutritional value to bees and is generally avoided by them.

Bees also visit flowers for another dietary reward produced by the plant: nectar. Nectar is a sugary plant secretion that also contains trace amounts of amino acids, proteins, lipids, and vitamins. It is bees' main dietary source of carbohydrates.

Flowers that require cross-pollination have evolved fascinating and beautiful ways to lure bees and other animals into collecting their pollen.

From a bee's perspective, these evolved traits are classified by four characteristics:

1. whether flowers have color patterns and aromas that are attractive;
2. whether the pollen can be readily released from the anther;
3. whether the protein content in the pollen is high enough to meet the bee's nutritional needs, and;
4. whether there is a nectar reward hidden in the flower.

Simply put, flowers that do not require cross-pollination are not attractive to bees. Humans have bred some flowers, such as tulips or daffodils, to be highly attractive to other humans, but bees have a different palette; a flower can look attractive to a bee, but if it doesn't yield high-quality pollen or have a nectar reward, it is just background decoration, not worthy of attention.

THE EVOLUTION OF BEE FLOWERS

Specifically, the flowers that are attractive to bees have evolved odors that are sweet and light. They have evolved color patterns that fall within the visual range of bees. Bees are not sensitive to light in the red spectrum, but they are sensitive to wavelengths in the ultraviolet spectrum. Some flowers have patches of color that contain ultraviolet reflectance that bees can see but humans cannot. Often these UV patches are arranged like landing lights, or nectar guides, on the petals, directing the bee into the rewarding reproductive parts of the flower. The color patterns of flowers also provide cues to passing bees about the quality and quantity of a flower's nectar.

The wells that secrete nectar, called *nectaries*, are strategically placed at the base of the reproductive structures of the flower. As a hungry bee reaches its tongue, or *proboscis*, into the nectary for some carbohydrate energy, the bee inadvertently deposits pollen collected from a previous flower she visited, resulting in pollination. The bee is rewarded with nectar, and the flower is rewarded with a little pollen that rubs off the bee. It's a win-win situation for both.

TABLE 4.1
Pollinator Syndromes

VECTOR	FLOWER SHAPE	FLOWER COLOR	SCENT	NECTAR QUALITY	POLLEN QUALITY	BLOOM TIME	EXAMPLES	NOTES
Melittophily I. (Bee pollination I.)	Simple, open, bowl-shaped	Blue, yellow, white	Variable, may include chemical attractants similar to bee sex pheromones	Variable	Variable. Sometimes sticky, or must be shaken from anthers	Day	Apple, sunflower, wild rose	Typically showy, flowers often have ultraviolet colored lines that guide bees towards nectar reward.
Melittophily II. (Bee pollination II.)	Complicated, asymmetrical petals	Blue, yellow, other	Variable, may include chemical attractants similar to bee sex pheromones	Variable	Variable. Sometimes sticky, or must be shaken from anthers	Day	Alfalfa, pea, orchid, penstemon	Like above, flowers are showy and often have ultraviolet colored lines which guide bees towards nectar reward.
Psychophily (Butterfly pollination)	Large, often with deep tubes or hidden nectar reservoirs	Pink, lavender, other	Often strong scented	Lots of nectar	Little pollen	Day	Milkweed, liatris, purple coneflower	Very showy, often with some sort of landing platform.
Phalaenophily (Moth pollination)	Large, often with deep tubes or hidden nectar reservoirs	Usually white	Often strong scented	Lots of nectar	Little pollen	Often night	Yucca, datura, morning glory	Moths may be diurnal or nocturnal depending on species, hence variable bloom times.
Myophily (Fly pollination I.)	Shallow, flat, open, or dish-shaped	White, yellow	Usually no strong scent	Little nectar	Little pollen	Day	Carrot, dill, parsnip, onion, yarrow	Often umbel-shaped flowers
Sapromyophily (Fly pollination II.)	Deep, tubular, or funnel-shaped	Brown or orange	Very strong, unpleasant odor similar to carrion or dung	Little nectar	Little pollen	Day and night	Skunk cabbage, red trillium	Flowers may be sticky, hairy, or include some other mechanism to temporarily trap and slow down visiting flies.
Cantharophily (Beetle pollination)	Large, flat, dish-shaped	Usually off-white, green, yellow	Strong scented, often spicy, fruity, or rotten smelling	Little nectar	Lots of pollen	Day and night	Magnolia, water lilies	Excess pollen often produced to compensate for feeding by beetles.
Ornithophily (Bird pollination)	Large, deep tubular, or funnel-shaped	Red, orange	No smell	Lots of nectar	Little pollen	Day	Cardinal flower, hibiscus, columbine	Usually very showy. Pollen grains may be very large and sticky.
Chiropterophily (Bat pollination)	Large, bell-shaped	White, or light colored	Sometimes sulfur scented	Lots of nectar	Little pollen	Night	Saguaro cactus, durian	Like bird-pollinated flowers, often very showy. Pollen grains may be very large and sticky.
Anemophily (Wind pollination)	Small, inconspicuous, feathery stigmas	Green	No smell	No nectar	Lots of pollen	Day and night	Pine, corn, other grasses	Often growing in large monocultures, often the tallest plants in a particular environment. Insects may consume pollen, but do not contribute to pollination.

5 Bumble Bees

Elaine Evans, *Author*—Befriending Bumble Bees

Around the world, bumble bees are given friendly nicknames such as humble bees, cow bees, and thunder bees. They are well known as large fuzzy bees dutifully flying from flower to flower (figure 5.1). These teddy bears of the insect world also play a vital role in production of many important crops. Bumble bee pollination improves the quality of tomatoes, cranberries, blueberries, and many other

Elaine Evans

Figure 5.1 Asters are a common autumn food source for bumble bees.

crops. As natives of North America, bumble bees are particularly well suited to pollinating our native flowers, flowers that provide food and shelter to countless other organisms.

Each bee species has its own unique attributes that suit them for pollinating their preferred flowers. To effectively use bumble bees as pollinators, it is important to understand the needs of the plants and what physical and behavioral characteristics bumble bees have to offer.

Bumble bee pollinating services are provided by both wild and managed bumble bee populations. Managed bumble bees are primarily available through commercial producers, although methods for raising your own colonies are available. Wild populations of many bumble bee species appear to be in decline worldwide. Possible causes of the declines include habitat loss, pesticides, climate change, pests, parasites, and disease.

Natural History of Bumble Bees

Worldwide, there are approximately 250 species of bumble bees. Over 40 bumble bee species are native to North America. Of these, only one species, *Bombus impatiens*, is currently reared by commercial producers in North America. Bumble bees vary greatly in size, with bees weighing from 40 to 830 milligrams

(0.0014 to 0.029 ounces). There is variety in size both among species and within species. There are three types of bumble bees: queens, workers, and males. Males and workers are similar in size, but the queens are much larger, sometimes three times the size of workers or males. Early in the season, when there are fewer workers in the colony to collect pollen, the workers are often smaller because their size depends on how much food the bees are fed as larvae. As the colony population grows, and more workers bring in more pollen, the colony will produce larger workers.

Bumble bees are social insects, living in colonies consisting of a queen and her offspring. As in most societies, through cooperation and division of labor, the social colony has greater productivity than the sum of each individual's abilities. Tasks are divided among the three types of bees. The queen's prime duty is to lay eggs. The workers collect food, tend the young, and clean and defend the nest. The male's sole purpose is to mate with queens.

Most of the queen's offspring are females. As with honey bee queens, the bumble bee queen has control over whether or not she fertilizes an egg. If

the egg is fertilized, it develops into a female. If the egg is unfertilized, it develops into a male. Females can be either queens or workers. Whether or not a female egg develops into a queen or worker is primarily dependent on the amount of food she is fed as a larva. Queens are significantly larger than workers and require much greater amounts of pollen (figure 5.2). Queens are usually only produced at the end of a colony cycle, when there are enough worker bees present in the colony to bring in sufficient amounts of pollen for queen development. Since queens are two to three times the size of workers, they require two to three times the amount of pollen for their development. Queens are the only females to mate and produce female offspring. Workers are able to lay eggs, but since workers do not mate, these eggs will become male. Most males are produced by the queen late in the colony cycle. For some species, the end of the colony cycle is midsummer, for others it is late summer.

Bumble Bee Life Cycle

Each spring, the fate of the summer's bumble bee population hangs tenuously on the ability of independent queen bumble bees to survive pests, predators, and inclement spring weather. Nests are begun anew each spring by queens who survived the winter, burrowed in the soil, protected from freezing by an antifreeze in their blood. Their first task once they emerge is to find a suitable nesting site. Some bumble bee species prefer to nest above ground, typically in clumps of grass. Other bumble bee species prefer to nest underground, typically in abandoned rodent nests. Since the queen is on her own, she must now find food both for herself and for her young. Early sources of pollen and nectar, such as willow, are essential to the survival of these queens. The survival of these queens, in turn, is essential for the summer's bumble bee population, as these queens produce all the workers of the summer.

The queen brings the pollen and nectar she collects back to the nest (figure 5.3). She has "pollen baskets," concave areas for pollen storage, on her back legs. She will pack pollen tightly into these baskets for transport back to the nest. Back in the nest, the queen forms the pollen into a clump onto

Elaine Evans

Figure 5.2 The bumble bee hive interior. The queen (center) is easy to identify by her large size. Most of the darker brown open wax cells contain nectar, while the lighter colored cells contain developing larvae or pupae.

Eric Mader

Figure 5.3 Like honey bees, foraging bumble bees store gathered pollen on their back legs. The leg indentation that holds this packed pollen is appropriately called the "pollen basket," or corbicula. The flower in this picture is Swamp Milkweed (*Asclepias incarnata*).

which she lays eggs. She drinks nectar from flowers and stores it in her "nectar crop," a holding tank in her abdomen. The queen will use wax, produced by glands on her abdomen, to form a pot to hold the nectar she has collected. Bumble bees collect only enough surplus nectar to last through a few days of inclement weather. They do not convert the nectar into honey, as do honey bees.

The queen will lay from eight to twelve eggs on the clump of pollen. She covers the eggs with wax. After three days, larvae emerge from the eggs. The larvae remain under the wax cover, which expands as the larvae rapidly grow (figure 5.4). The rapid larvae growth is fueled by the nectar and pollen fed to them by the queen. After around fourteen days, the

Elaine Evans

Figure 5.4
Bumble bee larvae inside a wax chamber. Unlike honey bees, bumble bees do not construct hexagon-shaped wax combs.

larvae spin cocoons and pupate. Pupae remain in the cocoons for several weeks, finally emerging as adults. These bees are usually all female worker bees. The queen finally has some relief. These workers begin to take over some of the colony maintenance duties, such as foraging for nectar and pollen, defending the colony, and feeding the young. The queen can now dedicate more of her time to laying eggs.

Bumble bee colonies will usually produce queens and males towards the end of the colony life cycle. The queens and males will leave the nest to mate. After mating the new queens enter hibernation, usually digging themselves several inches down into the ground, where they will survive the winter. All other colony members, including the old queen, die off in the fall, leaving the hibernating new queens as the only link to the next generation of bees.

Bumble Bee as Managed Pollinators

When farms were smaller and set within a more diverse landscape, wild native bees provided pollination services for many crops. With strong pollinator populations and smaller field sizes, some farmers relied on the pollination services provided by native bees. As agriculture has moved towards larger fields with less surrounding wild area, farmers have become more dependent on bringing honey bees in to pollinate their crops. Their large colonies and ease of transportation make them an effective and relatively easy-to-use pollinator. However, it is never wise to rely on only one method for a service as important as pollination. Bumble bee colonies are not as easy to raise as honey bees. Bumble bee colonies do not usually contain more than 300 bees compared to 30,000 bees in a honey bee colony. However, bumble bees make up for these shortcomings in their extreme efficiency as pollinators. Characteristics that make bumble bees great pollinators include long tongues in some species, ability to fly in cold weather and low light, ability to buzz pollinate, and ease of use in greenhouse conditions.

Tongue Length

One of the most variable features between different species of bumble bees is tongue length. Bumble bee tongue lengths range from $^3/_{16}$ to $^{19}/_{32}$ inch (~5 to 15 millimeters). Tongue length is an important consideration as it directly affects a bee's ability to access nectar from flowers. Some flowers have a narrow tube with nectar at the bottom. To achieve pollination, the bee's tongue must be long enough to reach the nectar at the bottom of the tube. When the bee enters the tube to access the nectar, she comes into contact with the pollen from that flower and will transport it to other flowers she visits, thus pollinating the flowers. Honey bees and bumble bees with shorter tongues, which are unable to reach the nectar, will sometimes bite a hole at the bottom of the flower to access the nectar. These bees are cheating the flowers. The bees receive nectar, but the bees do not come into contact with the reproductive parts of the flower and so are not providing effective pollination services in return for this nectar. This is why bumble bees with long tongues are often preferred for pollinating flowers with long tubes.

An example of a crop that does well with long-tongued bees is red clover. Red clover flowers have tubes that are $^{19}/_{64}$ inch (~7.5 millimeters) or deeper. Honey bees have a tongue length of only $^{15}/_{64}$ to ¼ inch (~5.9 to 6.25 millimeters). Honey bees can reach the red clover nectar if they push their heads into the tube and if the nectar level is high. Although honey bees will visit red clover for pollen, which is more easily accessible, they cannot be relied on to consistently visit red clover. If there are other flowers with accessible nectar, the honey bees will focus their foraging efforts on those plants. Long-tongued bumble bees have no trouble reaching the nectar at the bottom of red clover flowers. However, short-tongued bumble bees will have the same difficulties as honey bees.

Environmental Conditions

Aside from working in a greenhouse, most pollinators are exposed to extremely variable working conditions. Cold, heat, rain, light levels, and wind can all affect the ability of bees to fly from flower to flower and perform their duties. Bumble bees tolerate extreme conditions better than many other pollinators.

Honey bees are not very active at temperatures below 50°F (10°C), whereas bumble bees will con-tinue to forage at temperatures as low as 45°F (7.2°C). While this difference may seem small, it can be significant for pollination. For example, some flowers, such as cucumber, watermelon, and raspberry, release their pollen early in the morning, making this the time when bee visitation is most effective. Bumble bees are more likely than honey bees to visit flowers in the cooler early morning. Since this coincides with pollen release from these plants, bumble bee visits are more effective. Bumble bees also forage in lower light conditions than honey bees, adding to their work hours.

Bumble bees are also tolerant of stronger winds than honey bees and will even forage in light rain. Because of these traits, bumble bees can be a more reliable pollinator for crops where inclement weather is likely. In this situation, bumble bees can be used as supplemental pollinators, filling in when other bees cannot tolerate the conditions.

Buzz Pollination

For many flowers, pollen is readily accessible to anything that goes near the anthers. This is easily seen when you put your nose into a flower to smell it and your nose emerges covered with pollen. Some flowers are more conservative with their pollen, making it accessible only to certain pollinators. One strategy is to have very small pores on the anthers, so that pollen is only released when the anther is shaken. There are 64 families of plants with at least one member using this pollen dispersal method, including species in such economically important plant families as Ericaceae, Fabaceae, Rubiaceae, and Solanaceae. Pollen is released when bees grab the anthers in their mandibles and vibrate the muscles in their thorax. The vibrations travel through to the anther, and the pollen is shaken out of the pores. The distinctly audible toot that accompanies this behavior is the cause of the name "buzz pollination."

Bumble bees are not alone in their ability to buzz pollinate. Most major bee families (Colletidae, Andrenidae, Halictidae, and Apidae) have members that "buzz." However, most of the bees currently managed for pollination do not buzz pollinate. This has led to the use of bumble bees for many crops that have improved fruit set with buzz pollination, such as tomatoes, peppers, and blueberries.

Body Size

Both pollinators and the flowers they pollinate vary greatly in size. Bees range in size from mere specks to creatures as large as a human thumb. In order for pollination to occur, bees must reach the anthers and pistils of the flowers. Bumble bees are larger than many other managed pollinators, $^{13}/_{32}$ to $1^{3}/_{16}$ inch (~10 to 30 millimeters). This suits them well for pollination of crops with larger flowers such as cotton, where bumble bees have been preferred due to the efficiency of their pollination.

Flight Patterns

When crops require cross pollination, the movement of pollinators within the field must be considered. Often crops are planted with one variety in one row and another variety in the next row. Bumble bees tend to have a more erratic flight pattern than honey bees. Honey bees often fly straight down rows. For hybrid crops where rows are planted with different varieties that require out-crossing, bumble bees facilitate the movement of pollen across these rows. For sunflowers, there is some indication that better pollination can be achieved by having both honey bees and other bees present than when either are used alone. It appears that the presence of other bees increases the chances of honey bees crossing rows, and so increasing cross pollination.

Greenhouses

Bumble bees are ideal for use in greenhouses. Their nests are easily transported and housed within greenhouses. Honey bees are also used in greenhouses, but there are several aspects of honey bee behavior that make this difficult. Honey bees communicate with each other about the quality, quantity, and location of floral resources. Through this communication, a honey bee colony is able to focus most of its foraging effort on the most highly productive flower patches. If the most rewarding resources are located outside the greenhouse, and there are vents open through which the bees can escape, honey bees will forage on those resources, ignoring the flowers in the greenhouse. Although bumble bees can also escape and forage elsewhere if greenhouse vents are open, bumble bees are more likely to focus their foraging efforts primarily on the resources that are most readily available.

Bumble bees are the primary pollinators used for most greenhouse tomatoes. Tomatoes form larger, more even fruits with buzz pollination. Before bumble bees became widely available through commercial producers, tomato flowers were pollinated either by honey bees or by vibrating machines operated manually. Bumble bees are much more efficient and much less expensive than the other options. The greenhouse tomato industry grew significantly after bumble bees became available commercially in the early 1990s. From the early 1990s to 2003, North American greenhouse tomato growing area is estimated to have increased by almost 600 percent to 4,260 acres (1,725 hectares).

Using Bumble Bees as Crop Pollinators

Bumble bees commonly pollinate over 25 crops worldwide, including cranberries, blueberries, strawberries, plums, zucchinis, melons, sweet peppers, tomatoes, as well as seed crops like alfalfa, red clover, cotton, and sunflower (see sidebar, page 48). While some crops may achieve sufficient pollination with only bumble bees present, others may achieve greatest pollination with a combination of bumble bees and other pollinators. Bumble bees can be used for pollination both in greenhouses and outdoors.

In the Greenhouse

Since greenhouses are enclosed environments, bumble bees must be supplied by domesticated colonies. In eastern North America, the species *Bombus impatiens* is still readily available for purchase for use in greenhouses (Figure 5.5, page 48).

In greenhouses, vents can be screened to prevent bee loss. Some greenhouses use UV-excluding film to reduce heat. Bumble bees see into the UV range and may use information from UV light for orientation. This may interfere with bumble bees' foraging patterns, though they will still forage and pollinate even with UV light excluded. Keep bumble bee colonies in the shade. Bumble bee colonies are usually insulated from high air temperatures by nesting in the ground. Temperatures over 90°F (32.2°C) can be damaging to

Elaine Evans

Figure 5.5 Bumble bee hives produced by commercial insectaries are typically made of cardboard with plastic internal components. A supplemental sugar syrup food source is included. These hives are typically used in greenhouse situations to pollinate high-value crops like hydroponic tomatoes.

developing brood. Exposure of bumble bees to pesticides used in greenhouses can be mitigated by closing the entrance to the bee colony before pesticides are applied. If the nest entrance is closed at night, most bees should be within the hive.

In the Field

There are two basic methods to use bumble bees for pollination in the field. The first is to rely on wild populations of bumble bees. This will be most effective if the field is relatively small and located in a diverse landscape, including undisturbed areas. Clearly, there must be a strong population of bumble bees in an area before they can be relied upon for pollination. Timing of crop bloom is also an important factor. In early spring, only queens will be out foraging. Once these queens establish nests, the number of available bees will drastically increase. One queen can produce colonies of 50 to 800 workers. By midsummer, bumble colonies should be well established with strong worker populations available for pollination. The landscape can be altered to encourage native bumble bees. One simple solution is to leave areas unmowed to provide better nesting habitat. Surrounding areas can be planted with flowers that

---

BOMBUS IMPATIENS

Bombus impatiens (figure 5.6) is currently the preeminent bumble bee for commercial pollination in North America. As a medium-tongued bee, the workers' tongue lengths range from $5/32$ to $15/64$ inch (~4 to 6 millimeters), similar to the size range of honey bee workers' tongues. Queens' tongues range from $25/64$ to $7/16$ inches (~10 to 11 millimeters) in length. This means that *B. impatiens* workers are not well suited as pollinators for flowers with deep tubes. *B. impatiens* queens emerge in early spring. The nests are usually formed underground. At the high point of colony development, colonies can contain upwards of 800 workers, though typical colonies will have 200 to 400 workers. If you live in an area where *B. impatiens* is native, it is an excellent candidate for your own rearing efforts.

Elaine Evans

Figure 5.6 *Bombus impatiens* is a common and widespread bumble bee in the midwest and eastern US. It is one of the most commonly reared species. Shown here with a hyssop flower.

provide a constant progression of blooming flowers, so that bumble bees are provided with the nectar and pollen they need to support each stage of their colony life cycle.

The second method is to use domesticated bumble bee colonies. There are several commercial producers of bumble bees that provide colonies year-round. These colonies can appear to be costly, but when the benefits of increased yield and fruit quality are taken into account, they are usually an economically beneficial option. You can also raise bumble bees yourself. This will require investments of equipment, space, and time. The rewards include not only pollinators for your crops, but a chance to get to know these fierce, humble creatures more intimately and learn more about how they live.

History of Bumble Bee Domestication

People began to explore the use of bumble bees for crop pollination in the late 19th century. Bumble bees were intentionally introduced from the UK to New Zealand, which had no native bumble bee species, in order to pollinate red clover plants used for livestock forage. Anyone using bumble bees for pollination at this time was relying on wild populations, as domestication methods had not yet been developed.

The first major breakthrough in bumble bee domestication came in 1912, when F.W.L. Sladen outlined methods for domesticating bumble bees in his book *The Humble Bee*. With domestication, farmers no longer needed to rely on sporadic wild populations. Bumble bee colonies could be produced and placed directly within crops to provide pollination. However, one major impediment to widespread use of bumble bees for pollination is that colonies could only be initiated from queens caught in the spring after emerging from hibernation. Colonies were only available from later spring through the fall. Bumble bees could not be used for early spring or winter blooming crops.

The second major breakthrough happened in the 1970s, when researchers developed the use of carbon dioxide gas to bring queens out of hibernation early, making it possible to initiate bumble bee colo-

nies at any time. This enabled commercial producers of bumble bees to have colonies available year-round. Bumble bees became the primary pollinator in greenhouses, particularly for tomatoes. Commercial producers, primarily in Europe, began marketing bumble bees worldwide. North American-based rearing facilities were founded in the 1990s, with one species being raised for use west of the Rockies (*Bombus occidentalis*) and one raised for use in eastern North America (*Bombus impatiens*).

In 1996, *Nosema*, a parasite that infects bumble bees, decimated western commercial facilities. It is thought that the infection may have stemmed from transport of a strain of *Nosema* from European bumble bee colonies. *B. occidentalis* is no longer viable as a commercially raised species. Wild populations of *B. occidentalis* and several other related species appear to have dropped dramatically soon afterwards. *B. occidentalis* was once a common species but is now rare throughout much of its former range. Eastern commercial facilities raising *B. impatiens* were not affected by this problem. *B. impatiens* is still available commercially. Since the collapse of western North American rearing facilities, there have been attempts to import eastern species into western states. Due to risks of disease or pest transmission, there has been opposition to these importations. The authors of this book adamantly believe it is best if local western species can be raised for use in western North America.

There are several lessons to be learned from the problems afflicting the honey bee industry: that international movement of bees carries with it the risk of spreading diseases and pests; and that pollination services provided by bees cannot be taken for granted. Since honey bees are not native to North America, there is no option to raise native, local honey bees. However, with over 45 different bumble bee species in North America, we have that option with bumble bees. To prevent the spread of diseases and pests that could decimate both commercial and wild bumble bee populations, it is crucial that local bumble bees are raised for use as pollinators. It is also important that we encourage natural bumble bee populations by providing suitable nesting habitat and ample forage.

Raising Bumble Bees

Bumble bee domestication is in relatively early stages of development as an industry. Currently, it is dominated by a few international companies. Methods have been industry secrets or have been buried in the scientific literature, not easily available to the public. Recent publication of a bumble bee rearing manual has made it possible for more people to get involved in raising bumble bees. There is great potential for individuals to work with rearing to supply colonies for pollination. The following is a summary of the basic principles of bumble bee rearing. More details can be found in *Befriending Bumble Bees* by Evans et al. (see page 150).

Catching Queens

Bumble bee species vary greatly in their ease of domestication. Of the over 250 bumble bee species in the world, there are only two that are currently reared commercially, though there is potential for many other species to be raised. In eastern North America, good candidates for rearing include *B. impatiens* and *B. bimaculatus*. In western North America, good candidates for rearing include *B. bifarius* and *B. vosnesenskii* (figure 5.7). Take the time and effort to learn how to identify your local bumble bee species (see sidebar). Some bumble bees are rare and should not be collected. *Bombus affinis, Bombus occidentalis, Bombus terricola, Bombus franklini, Bombus sonorus,*

Elaine Evans

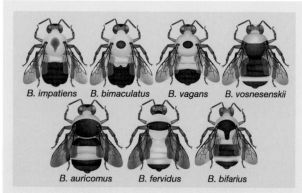

B. impatiens B. bimaculatus B. vagans B. vosnesenskii

B. auricomus B. fervidus B. bifarius

Figure 5.7 Common bumble bees of North America. Queens look much the same as workers, except that queens are slightly larger. *Bombus impatiens* is the most commonly reared bumble bee in the eastern US. *Bombus vosnenskii* and *B. bifarius* are good candidates for rearing among western bumble bees.

Bombus pensylvanicus, and *Bombus ashtoni* populations have dropped in recent years. If you find a rare specimen, please leave it in the wild but take a photo to help document its population status (send the photo to: www.bugguide.net or bumblebees@xerces.org).

IDENTIFYING BUMBLE BEES

Many bumble bees can be identified easily by their color patterns. Some require closer examination. It is helpful to closely examine specimens as you are learning to identify them. Take an ice chest out to the field and slow bees down by cooling them for a few minutes. The bees will recover unharmed after they warm up, but while they are slowed down, you can examine them more closely.

Here are a few great resources for identifying North American bumble bees.

Golick, D. A. and M. D. Ellis. 2000. *Bumble Boosters: A Guide to the Identification of Nebraska Bumble Bee Species.* University of Nebraska Press.

Griffin, B. L. 1997. *Humblebee Bumblebee.* Knox Cellar Publishing. Bellingham, WA.

Heinrich, B. 1979. *Bumble Bee Economics.* Harvard University Press.

Kearns, C. A. and J. D. Thompson. 2001. *The Natural History of Bumble Bees, a Sourcebook for Investigations.* University Press of Colorado.

Thorp, R. W., D. S. Horning, Jr., and L. L. Dunning. 1983. *Bumble Bees and Cuckoo Bumble Bees of California.* Bulletin of the California Insect Survey. Volume 23: 1–79.

Elaine Evans

To successfully raise bumble bees, the most important element is a supply of bumble bee queens. Only mated queen bees are capable of producing an entire colony of bees. Once your rearing system is established, you can supply yourself with your own queens. Before this, you will need to capture wild bumble bee queens. Some people set out empty boxes with the hope of attracting wild nesting bumble bee queens. Even with hundreds of boxes, the success rates reported are typically very small. Finding queens while they forage on flowers is the most reliable method for collecting them. Spring favorites of bumble bee queens include honeysuckle, dandelion, mountain laurel, clover, rhododendron, Siberian pea, horse chestnut, Virginia waterleaf, mint, apples, cherries, willows, and gooseberry.

Queens are the only bumble bees that hibernate through the winter. Search for them after they have emerged from hibernation and before they start a nest on their own. Different species have different emergence times, but in North America, most will emerge between March and July. Queens with established nests will have pollen loads. Capture only bees with no pollen loads.

Caring for Your Queen

Now that you have your queen, place her in an environment that will encourage her to begin laying eggs. Many different housing designs are suitable for raising bumble bees. Often queens are placed in a small box until they lay eggs (figure 5.8). After workers have emerged, they are moved to a larger box. Boxes can be made of any material that is hard enough to resist the strong mandibles of bumble bees. Wood is the most commonly used material. Plexiglas® can be used to enable better viewing inside the nest. Heavy cardboard and poured plaster are also possible construction materials. If your colony is to be placed outside to forage freely, all sides should be wood or some other opaque material, with a few small screen-covered ventilation holes, so that the nest stays dark. Nest boxes can also be buried underground or in sand with an entrance tube connecting the colony to the outside. This can help the bees maintain favorable temperatures and humidity in their nests. It also will help conceal the nest from predators.

Figure 5.8 A queen starter box. The queen is transferred to the box through the sliding front door. The metal cover keeps the brood-rearing area dark and can be removed to observe the queen. Nectar is supplied by a wick through the floor.

Provide the queen with nectar and pollen as she establishes her nest. Sugar solutions make excellent nectar substitutes. Place the solution in some kind of closed dispenser. Bees may accidentally drown in an open liquid source. For dispensing from the top or side, use a bottle with a very small opening (some use a syringe), so that only one drop forms at a time. For dispensing through the floor, a feeder is set below the floor of the starter box with a wick protruding through the floor; cotton wicks are available through dental supply stores (figure 5.9, page 52).

Supply the queen with a pea-sized pollen ball. The pollen used to make the "pollen ball" should be as fresh as possible, ideally frozen as soon as possible after collection from the honey bees and used within a month or two. Contact a local honey bee beekeeper to buy fresh pollen from them. One-half pound (0.23 kilograms) of pollen per colony should be more than enough to raise a colony to the point where they can forage independently. Replace the pollen ball every few days unless there is evidence of eggs having been laid on it. Once larvae hatch, provide fresh pollen on a regular basis. Developing colonies will need an amount of pollen equal to roughly one-third of

Elaine Evans

Figure 5.9 A simple nectar feeder consisting of a dental wick and plastic container. The feeder is placed below the starter box with the wick protruding through the floor.

the size of the brood area each day. The brood area includes the wax cells occupied by eggs, larvae, and pupae.

Bumble bee colonies are usually raised in a dark environment with 50 percent relative humidity, at temperatures above 70°F (21.1°C). If you cannot keep the room warm, be sure that you provide the queen with insulating material. Upholsterer's cotton is the ideal material. Do not substitute cotton balls, as the bees will become tangled in the fibers.

Handling Mature Colonies

It is useful to have at least one extra cover for your bumble bee box that is made of clear plastic with a hole in the center. The hole should be large enough for your hand to fit through (figure 5.10). By using a solid sheet of plastic in combination with the cut sheet, you can gain access to the colony without letting bees escape. Place the solid piece of plastic on top of the sheet with the hole. When you see that no bees are flying or moving near the top, slide the solid piece off, giving you access to the hive. A pair of blunt-ended tweezers is the best tool for grabbing bees from the nest. With experience and patience, you can gently pick them up by the back legs without causing them any harm. It is also helpful to keep some small jars in the bumble bee room to trap any escaped bees. If you use only red light in the rooms where you work with the bees, the bees are less likely

to fly out of the nest. Bumble bees do not see the red spectrum, so a red light disturbs them less than the typical lights we use in our homes.

Before you open colonies to the outside to forage freely, there are several things to consider. It is important to wait until the colony is strong, meaning there are at least 20 workers present, before letting them have access to the outside. Even then, the bees may require some food supplementation until they get used to foraging. Provide all colonies with nectar and pollen during the first week of their release. After this, monitor the nest occasionally to make sure they have enough food. If placing the box outside, place it in the shade. Secure the lid so that it will not blow off in the wind. More protection may be needed if there are skunks or bears in the area.

Queen Mating and Hibernation

Colonies produce queens and males at the end of the colony's life cycle (figure 5.11). Signs of queen production are enlarged cells containing queen pupae and the production of males. Males can be distinguished by longer antennae and a lack of pollen baskets on the hind legs. It is possible to allow queens

Elaine Evans

Figure 5.10 A wooden bumble bee hive box with the lid removed. A piece of clear plastic with a hole in the center allows for observation and supplemental feeding of the colony. The lid is also made of clear plastic.

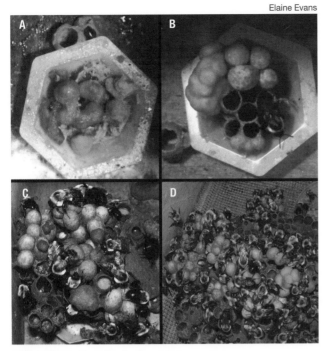

Elaine Evans

Figure 5.11 Growth of a bumble bee colony.

Stage 1: Colony initiation. Eggs and young larvae develop in wax cells. (A)

Stage 2: Multiple generations. The earliest laid eggs have developed into pupae, which will soon emerge as adult workers. Additional eggs and larvae continue to develop. (B)

Stage 3: Continual worker production. The new workers assume care of developing eggs and larvae. These workers also take over the foraging duties of the queen. Her only task now is to lay more eggs. (C)

Stage 4: Reproductive phase. Late in the season new queens begin to emerge from larvae that were better fed than earlier generations of workers. Males also begin to emerge. The main colony will soon die. (D)

produced by a colony to mate in confinement with males from another colony and then store queens in a refrigerator with the temperature set between 30° and 40°F (-1.1° and 4.4°C), mimicking winter hibernation. This procedure will provide you with fertil-

Table 5.1 Bumble Bee Pests and Parasites	
PESTS AND PARASITES	DAMAGE
Wax moths (*Galleria mellonella, Aphomia sociella,* and *Vitula edmandsii*)	Destroys nest structure
Small hive beetles (*Aethina tumida*)	Eats pollen, destroys nest structure
Parasitic bumble bees (*Bombus* spp., subgenus: *Psithyrus*)	Kills queen, has colony raise her offspring
Parasitic wasps (*Melittobia* spp.)	Kills larvae and pupae, can destroy colony
Parasitic mites (*Locustacarus buchneri*)	Infects adults, transmits viruses
Single-celled internal parasites (*Nosema bombi, Crithidia bombi,* and *Apicystis bombi*)	Infects adults, can destroy colony
Internal roundworms (*Spaerularia bombi*)	Infects queens, can prevent egg-laying

ized queens whenever you need them. Year-round production of bumble bee colonies depends on this year-round access to queens.

Protecting Your Colonies' Health

Keep an eye on the health of your colonies. There are pests, parasites, and diseases that can have deleterious effects on your colonies (see table 5.1). There are also scavengers and others that do no harm or can actually benefit your colonies. It is important to properly identify other creatures you find residing in bumble bee colonies. Promptly isolate any colonies experiencing sudden drops in population. If reusing equipment, be sure to sterilize before reuse.

6 Mason Bees

Eric Mader, *Pollinator Outreach Coordinator, the Xerces Society for Invertebrate Conservation*

Many current mason bee management practices are the result of previous research with the alfalfa leafcutter bee, *Megachile rotundata* (see chapter 7, page 75). The two groups of bees have similar life cycles, nesting requirements, and management techniques. However, while the alfalfa leafcutter bee has been managed for decades, mason beekeeping is still relatively new—having only been practiced on a commercial scale in the US since the 1990s. Earlier mason beekeeping occurred in Japan, where the native hornfaced bee (*Osmia cornifrons*), has been maintained as an orchard pollinator since the 1940s. Currently, 80 percent of the apples grown in Japan's Aomori prefecture (Japan's largest apple growing region) are pollinated by the hornfaced bee (see sidebar, page 56).

Because of their similarities, mason bees and alfalfa leafcutter bees share many of the same kinds of parasites, diseases, and other management problems. Unfortunately, most mason beekeepers are relatively inexperienced with these problems and maintain bees in conditions that would be unacceptable to experienced leafcutter producers. Individuals interested in keeping mason bees should review the leafcutter chapter of this book (pages 75–93), noting the factors that resulted in the decline of that industry in the US.

Natural History

Like the alfalfa leafcutter bee, mason bees belong to the family Megachilidae. As with other members of the Megachilidae family, mason bees use their large, scissor-like jaws to gather mud, pieces of leaf, or flower petals for the construction of their nests. All species of mason bee currently managed in the US belong to the genus *Osmia*. There are several hun-

Scott Bauer, USDA

Figure 6.1 *Osmia* sp. on flower.

dred members of the Megachilidae family in North America, and dozens of members of the *Osmia* genus (including both native and nonnative bees). Currently only three species—*Osmia lignaria, Osmia californica,* and *Osmia cornifrons*—are commonly available from commercial suppliers. Other *Osmia* species are managed regionally.

All *Osmia* are solitary, meaning that each female bee independently constructs her own nest, provisions the nest with pollen, and lays eggs. There is no queen, and the bees do not live together as a social unit like honey bees do. Female *Osmia* do not interact with other bees or with their own offspring after laying their eggs.

Many *Osmia* are gregarious, however, meaning that they have a tendency to construct their nests near each other—hence large numbers of bees can be housed in a single structure containing multiple nests. Many *Osmia* species will nest in manmade nests, however most species are difficult to domesticate because they are not gregarious. Male bees have no role in the construction or the provisioning of nests. Upon their emergence as adults, males mate, then die soon thereafter. While they may feed on small amounts of flower nectar to maintain their own energy, male bees do not actively collect pollen, and have little value as pollinators.

Most native *Osmia* are ⁹⁄₃₂ to ¹⁹⁄₃₂ inch in length (~7 to 15 millimeters) with male bees noticeably smaller than females. The majority of North American species are metallic blue, black, or green in color although other color variations exist. All female *Osmia* have parallel rows of pollen collecting hairs, called the scopa, on the underside of their abdomen. Female bees also typically have a pair of horn-like projections on the lower face. Male bees do not have facial horns, but often have longer antennae and a distinctive tuft of white hair in the center of their face (figure 6.2).

Despite having a stinger, female mason bees are not aggressive and rarely sting, even when handled. The sting is also much less painful than that of a honey bee. As a result beekeepers do not need any special protective equipment when working with *Osmia*. Male bees have round abdomens with no scopa or stinger (figure 6.3).

Figure 6.2 Like males of other mason bees, *Osmia aglaia* have a white patch of hair on the front of the face, and longer antennae.

Figure 6.3 Size comparison from left to right: *Osmia atriventris* (female), *O. cornifrons* (male), *O. cornifrons* (female), *O. lignaria* (male), *O. lignaria* (female), *O. lignaria* (female), *Apis mellifera* (female).

The most commonly managed mason bee, *Osmia lignaria,* is a temperate species native to most western states from southern Alaska south to California and eastward to Texas and Montana—and to most eastern states from Maine south to northern Georgia. The eastern and western bees comprise two distinct subspecies *Osmia lignaria propinqua* in the West, and *Osmia lignaria lignaria* in the East. Few records of the bee exist in the central plains states, probably due to an absence of suitable nesting habitat, although intermediate forms between the two subspecies have been reported.

Osmia lignaria is commonly called the Blue Orchard Bee, or "BOB" for short. Female BOBs are roughly the size of honey bees, although rounder in shape and metallic blue (figure 6.4, page 56). Male BOBs are similar but smaller with the characteristic tuft of white facial hair common to many *Osmia* species. BOBs are univoltine, meaning only one generation of

Mace Vaughan

Figure 6.4 A female blue orchard bee (*Osmia lignaria*) closes the entrance to her nest with mud.

offspring is produced each year. Currently, only the western subspecies of the BOB is commercially available from bee producers.

The second most commonly managed mason bee, *Osmia cornifrons*, or the hornfaced bee, is originally native to Japan. It was purposefully imported in the 1970s as a managed pollinator by the USDA Bee Lab in Beltsville, Maryland (see sidebar, below). Hornfaced bees are slightly smaller than the native BOB, and unlike many native *Osmia*, are brown in color with a striped abdomen and yellow scopa (as opposed to metallic blue or green). Like the BOB, the female hornfaced bee has a pair of horn-like prongs

NEW USE FOR A MULTI-TALENTED BEE

While the hornfaced bee is typically associated with tree fruit production, its potential on other crops is only recently being appreciated by a handful of people. Dr. Todd West, an assistant professor of horticulture at West Virginia University (WVU) is one of them. With support from USDA-SARE he has initiated an ambitious project that is introducing the bee to an entirely new group of fruit growers.

"Hornedfaced bees have the potential to be very useful and sustainable pollinators for blueberry production by small farmers in the Northeast Region of the US," says West. "As compared to honey bees, which require year-round maintenance, the hornfaced bee requires minimal input and management. The hornfaced bees are only active for six to eight weeks from April to June which coincides with blueberry blossom time."

As part of the program over 300 blueberry growers have been surveyed, and some will be provided with hornfaced bee cocoons and all of the necessary materials for management. The likes, dislikes, successes, and failures of those growers will be tracked and recorded over a two-year period. "Growers need to understand how to properly manage the bees and that the management practices are different than those of the honey bee," he says.

So far the results have been promising. "Initial research trials in West Virginia indicate that popu-

lation increases are possible with blueberry as the main pollen source." But as with other mason beekeepers, West concedes that there are some significant management challenges ahead. "The main limiting factor that we have encountered is mite infestations in the paper tube nesting system. These mite infestations have a direct negative effect on bee populations."

Ongoing research is being conducted at WVU to determine how to properly manage these mites, as well as trials of various commercially available nest systems.

West's advice to blueberry growers interested in trying hornfaced bees for pollination?

"I would suggest to anyone interested in managing hornfaced bees to make sure that you use secure storage methods to ensure that your bee population is parasite free. Setting the bees out in the field at the beginning of blueberry bloom is also crucial."

For more information contact:

Dr. Todd West
West Virginia University
Division of Plant and Soil Sciences
1090 Agriculture Sciences Building
Morgantown, WV 26506-6108
Phone: (304) 293-6023 ext. 4336
Email: Todd.West@mail.wvu.edu

protruding from the lower face, hence the common name. Also like the BOB, the hornfaced bee is univoltine, meaning one generation per year. Hornfaced bees are not as widely available as the BOB, and most managed populations exist in eastern and midwestern states. Feral hornfaced bees have been reported in some areas. The least common commercially available *Osmia* species is *Osmia californica*. This species resembles the BOB, but emerges later in the season, and is parsivoltine—meaning that some individual adults emerge after one year, while others emerge after two years of dormancy. This species also uses masticated leaf pulp, mud, and nectar in its nest construction, as opposed to only mud used by the BOB and hornfaced bee. *Osmia californica* is native to the western US.

With the exception of *Osmia californica*, most managed mason bees are only active in early spring. Adult bees emerge from eggs laid the previous spring. The bees are active for only a few weeks, during which they mate, construct nests, lay eggs, then die. The larvae slowly transform into adults over the summer, and they remain as dormant adults through the winter inside their nest until the following spring.

Because BOBs and hornfaced bees are only active in the early spring, their practical application is limited mostly to early blooming fruit crops. Despite this, they are sometimes advertised as "garden pollinators" in various garden supply catalogs. A gardener depending on these species to pollinate late-blooming vegetables will have little success without significant manipulation of the bees' natural lifecycle.

Lifecycle

Osmia are tunnel-nesting insects (figure 6.5). In the wild they nest beneath rock or bark crevices, in the hollow stems of pithy twigs, or in tunnels formed by

Spike Naughton

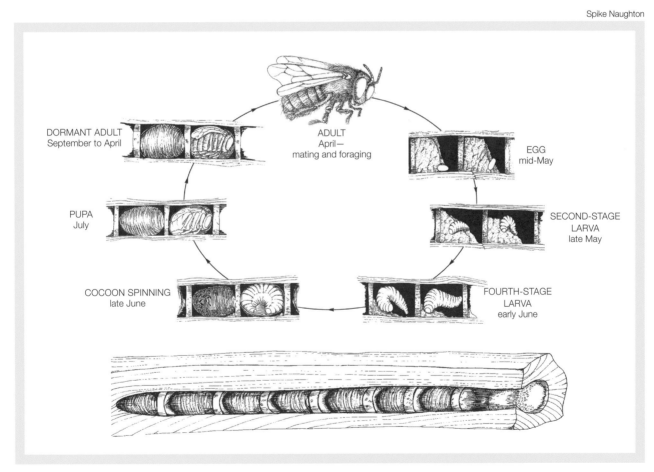

Figure 6.5 Lifecycle of the blue orchard bee in northern states (development and emergence time may be earlier in southern states).

wood-boring insects. A lack of nesting sites of this type limits the size of wild populations. Management systems exploit this nesting behavior by providing artificial nests constructed of blocks of wood drilled with multiple holes, bundles of cardboard straws, or sections of reed and bamboo. In the absence of suitable nest tunnels, some *Osmia* will construct amorphous mud structures within which to lay eggs.

When searching for a suitable nest site, a female bee may repeatedly enter and inspect numerous cavities. Tunnel depth, diameter, and material all influence the ratio of male-to-female eggs. After selecting a nest hole, she will then fly in a zigzag pattern in front of the nest entrance, memorizing its exact location. During this orientation flight, the bee memorizes adjacent visual landmarks that help her locate the nest later. It is also believed that female *Osmia* mark the nests they select with a pheromone to warn other bees that the nest is in use, and to identify the entrance later. After memorizing the location, the bee will be disoriented if the nest is moved—often causing her to completely abandon it. Prior to actual nest construction the female will also clean the tunnel of any dust or refuse. This behavior is occasionally observed even when extremely clean nest tubes are provided, and may be equivalent to the broody nesting behaviors observed in birds.

After memorizing the tunnel, the bee will then fly off in search of suitable materials to begin nest construction. *Osmia* construct the inner nest cavities with mud gathered in their jaws, literally building tiny cement walls—hence the common term "mason bees." The mud they prefer is soft and damp with a high clay content that can be molded and shaped without easily crumbling. Mason bees may burrow down through several inches of soil to find clay of the dampness and consistency they prefer. If mud is not available, other materials are sometimes substituted. Japanese beekeepers have observed hornfaced bees use masticated leaf pulp and bird droppings.

Upon finding suitable mud, the female bee will gather a small amount in her mandibles and front legs then fly back to the nest cavity where it is deposited at the innermost end. This mud is then formed into a wall-like partition. Up to a dozen collection trips may be necessary to gather enough mud to construct this inner wall, and the inner wall is nearly always built—even when a secure terminal wall already exists. Occasionally this wall may be built in the center of the cavity, especially in cavities over 7 inches deep (17.8 centimeters).

With this first wall complete, the female bee will begin collecting the provision of pollen and nectar that will feed her offspring. This process may require about 75 separate flower visits for each trip back to the nest. During these foraging trips, the female bee is repeatedly dusted with pollen that remains trapped among the hairs covering her body. Periodically she will groom herself, transferring pollen from the front of her body downward with her forelegs, to the middle legs, and finally to the hind legs, which scrape the pollen onto the scopa—the rows of long stiff hairs on the base of the abdomen that hold the pollen granules during the flight back to the nest. The bee also collects nectar that is stored in her crop, or "honey stomach." Upon returning to the nest, the bee will enter headfirst and regurgitate the nectar at the back of the cell. She will then somersault inside the nest if there is sufficient room, or she will back out of the nest, turn around and walk in backwards. She then scrapes the pollen from her scopa using her back legs and tamps the pollen-nectar food paste into a sloped pile using the tip of her abdomen.

A total of 15 to 40 foraging trips may be required to gather the necessary pollen and nectar to provision one cell, thus resulting in potentially thousands of flower visits. Under warm, clear conditions with unlimited forage, a bee may visit up to 25 flowers a minute and provision a single cell in a matter of hours.

When the food pile within the nest is of the appropriate size, the bee makes a final foraging trip to collect only nectar. This nectar is regurgitated onto the sloping front surface of the pile. The bee then backs out of the nest, turns around, and re-enters the nest backwards with the tip of her abdomen positioned over the sticky food mixture. She then lays a single egg directly into the pile. Eggs of the BOB and hornfaced bee are typically around 5/32 inch in length (4 millimeters), white, and sausage shaped. During egg laying, the bee may vibrate her flight muscles, creating a buzzing sound audible from outside the nest.

After laying the egg, the mother bee immediately begins to collect mud again to create a second wall that will completely enclose the developing egg. When the egg hatches, the larva will consume the pollen-nectar food provision and develop into an adult bee. The mother bee has no interaction with her offspring. The mud walls form a protective barrier against predators. If mud is readily available, the collection trips may take only one to two minutes. The pollen and nectar collection trips take longer, and may last for 10 or 15 minutes, even with floral sources closely available.

After closing off this first cell, the mother bee will then immediately begin construction of a second cell, repeating the process until the entire tunnel is almost filled. Depending on the length of the nest cavity, four to twelve cells may be constructed in a single tunnel. When the tunnel is nearly filled with cells, the bee then leaves an empty space near the entrance and constructs a final, thicker mud wall roughly flush with the opening (figure 6.6). The empty chamber provides an additional defense against predators such as wasps—some of which can penetrate mud walls with long ovipositors to lay their own eggs within the nest.

Under favorable conditions, a female BOB or horn-faced bee may live up to a month and complete one to six nest tunnels, with an average of around five to fifteen eggs in total—although 30 or more eggs have been documented in some cases. Of course during this nesting period the bee is exposed to predation by birds and predatory insects, inclement weather, pesticides, and a host of other conditions that can halt nesting activities at any moment. Female bees spend the evening inside the nest, facing inwards. Under overcast conditions, during rain, or when temperatures drop below 55°F (12.8°C) females will remain inside the nest but face outward, guarding against intrusion by other insects. Often in the early morning when it is too cold for active flight, female *Osmia* sit near the nest entrance facing outwards while warming their body.

As with other bee species, female *Osmia* store sperm in a specialized organ called the spermatheca. The spermatheca allows the mother bee to determine the sex of her offspring by either fertilizing an egg, resulting in a female offspring, or not fertilizing an egg, resulting in a male offspring. Female nest cells are larger and provisioned with more food. Normally, female eggs are laid in the innermost cells, and male eggs (because they are more expendable) are laid in the outermost cells closest to the entrance where parasite and predation rates may be higher. Sex ratio is determined in large part by the depth and diameter of the nest cavity, with deeper tunnels favoring the production of more female bees. Under optimal conditions sex ratios should be close to 1.5 to 2 males per female, with slightly more female offspring produced early in the nesting season.

Development time for the bee larvae is somewhat temperature dependent with warm spring temperatures resulting in slightly faster growth. Under ambient outdoor spring temperatures it takes about one week for the eggs to hatch. The first subsequent growth stage is not noticeably different from the egg to the unaided eye. This first *instar*—or immature grub—is fed by the egg yolk, and does not actively feed on the pollen-nectar food provision left by the mother bee.

After roughly another week, the immature bee molts by shedding its skin-like exoskeleton, emerging as a larger grub, discernibly different from the initial

G. Neuenswander

Figure 6.6 Recently completed blue orchard bee nest in a reed section. The first three cells (left) contain larger pollen-nectar provisions and female eggs. Male eggs are on smaller provisions in the last four cells. Note the empty cell and mud plug at the nest entrance (right). This empty cell provides an additional barrier against nest intrusion by predators and parasites.

instar. At this stage the head of the grub descends into the food mixture and begins actively feeding. In total the larva undergoes five growth molts over a period of roughly one month. The final larval stage is $^{15}/_{32}$ to $^{43}/_{64}$ inch in length (~12 to 17 millimeters) depending on temperature, quality of food, nest size, and sex—with females being larger than males.

Upon reaching the final larval stage, the immature bee has usually eaten all of the food provision in the nest. It will then defecate and spin a tough silk cocoon produced by its salivary glands (figure 6.7). During the cocoon spinning process, the larva's head will rotate continuously within the nest chamber as the nearly invisible thread is wrapped around its body. After several days a tough dark-colored silk pellet, often covered with fecal residue, is all that remains (figure 6.8). Under normal conditions, development will then cease, and the bee will remain in this dormant prepupal stage throughout much of the summer. In midsummer, the immature bee again molts into a white pupa within the cocoon. These pupae resemble adult bees, except they are completely white in color (figure 6.9). After another month, the pupa molts again inside the cocoon, shedding the

G. Neuenswander

Figure 6.9 Left to right: blue orchard bee prepupae, white pupa (side view), and black pupa (ventral view) in cut cocoons.

Karen Strickler

Figure 6.10 Cocoons of *O. lignaria* (top row) and *O. cornifrons* (bottom row). The *O.lignaria* cocoons tend to be slightly fuzzier and brown or gray in color. The cocoons of *O. cornifrons* are smooth and gold. The dark specks are fecal pellets.

D.F. Veirs

Figure 6.7 Three blue orchard bee nests with cocoons in paper straws. Nest entrances with empty cells and mud plugs are to the right. Note large female cocoons in the innermost cells (left) and smaller male cocoons in outermost cells. From top to bottom, the numbers of female cocoons are four, three, and two, respectively.

Eric Mader

Figure 6.8 A cut-away view of a bamboo nest tube reveals the *Osmia cornifrons* cocoons within. The large innermost cocoons are female.

translucent pupal skin. The fully formed adult bee within the cocoon remains dormant throughout the winter (figure 6.10).

All managed *Osmia* species require exposure to cold winter temperatures for successful emergence the following spring. The duration of this exposure depends on the species and the local conditions under which the managed population originated.

Emergence begins as temperatures warm the following spring. Male emergence always precedes female emergence, and usually at least 50 percent of all male bees will have emerged prior to the first female. The process may last several weeks. Emergence activity is particularly frequent during midmorning on sunny days.

Emerging bees use their strong scissor-like jaws to chew through their silk cocoon and mud wall nest partitions. Bees located in the deepest nest cells may have to push or chew their way through debris left by nest mates nearer the entrance. Dead bees within the nest create an obstacle that other bees, located deeper inside, must chew their way through. This process can result in the spread of diseases like chalkbrood or parasitic mites. Upon emergence, bees often bask for several minutes in the sunlight before flying.

Mating occurs near the nest from which the bees emerged, with male bees pouncing on the backs of newly emerged females, often before they can fly, grasping them with their legs. Female bees may release a pheromone to attract male mates. If the female bee is receptive, she will raise the tip of her abdomen and invert her stinger, allowing coupling. Mating lasts less than a minute, and bees may mate repeatedly. Sperm is retained in the spermatheca while the ovaries mature. Within one to two days the female is ready to lay eggs. During this period she will feed on nectar and find and orient to a suitable nest tunnel.

Female bees prefer to nest near sites from which they themselves emerged, although not necessarily in the same cavity. Despite this, some female bees will abscond from the area after mating in a process referred to as pre-nesting dispersal. As a general rule, the more appealing the nest site, the fewer females will disperse prior to nesting.

Obtaining and Handling Bees: Trap Nesting vs. Purchasing

A common way of obtaining mason bees is by trap-nesting wild populations. Trap nests are set out in the fall or winter in locations that have good numbers of wild bees, then the nests are removed the following summer. Ideal locations to place nests are on the sides of old barns or wooden farm structures, adjacent to cliff faces, or near other large visual landmarks (figure 6.11). Nests can be hung inside open sheds and garages or on south- and east-facing walls. Nests should be shielded from rain and direct sunlight (figure 6.12).

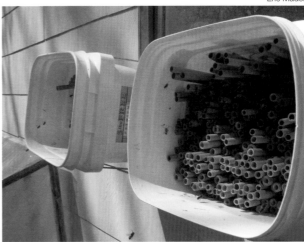

Figure 6.11 Nests should ideally be placed against the walls of barns, garages, or other large landmarks in bright but indirect sunlight. The irregular lengths, diameters, and colors of these bamboo nest tubes are extremely appealing to mason bees.

Figure 6.12 This typical nest shelter is located against an east-facing wall to encourage flight activity early in the day.

Note for figure 6.12: The covered bucket in the upper left hand corner contains filled nest tubes from the previous season. Bees exit through the single hole, where they find the new, clean nest tubes in the adjacent buckets. The yellow bucket buried in front of the shelter holds mud for nest construction. Although the chicken wire provides protection against marauding woodpeckers, it discourages bees and should only be used when necessary.

Floral sources are also an important consideration when selecting an area to trap wild *Osmia*. Overgrown abandoned pastures and early-succession meadows with sufficient flowers are especially good and support wild populations of bees. Spring-flying mason bees (such as BOBs) in particular require early-blooming pollen and nectar sources such as willow, cherry, chokecherry, spring flowering raspberries and blackberries, hawthorn, currants, gooseberries, waterleaf, and various penstemon species (figure 6.13).

Ideally nests in wild areas should be camouflaged and marked with the owner's name. Trap nesting of alfalfa leafcutter bees on public land in western states has occasionally led to theft of bee nests.

G. Neuenswander

Figure 6.13 A typical mason bee nest shelter in a blooming cherry orchard.

A COMMERCIAL PRODUCER'S PERSPECTIVE

In addition to his duties as a lecturer at the University of Washington, Evan Sugden is the owner of Entomo-Logic, a company that produces blue orchard bees and rearing hardware. In the following interview Dr. Sugden discusses his experiences in the bee ranching business, and offers his perspective on the challenges facing this new industry.

1. How did you decide to go into the mason bee business?

My interest in solitary bee production and management was a logical and progressive outgrowth of my training and interests. I received an undergraduate degree in biology and ultimately a PhD in entomology from U. C. Davis specializing in bee biology and pollination. I have held bee-related positions since then, working in government, private industry, and university research. My official focus has been on honey bees, but since my graduate period I have maintained a strong interest in solitary bee ecology. Twelve years ago I moved to the Pacific Northwest where blue orchard bees are abundant in nature. I had time outside of my regular employment at the University of Washington to delve into bee management and was soon producing significant numbers of bees, researching management problems, and cooperating with other producers and scientists in the field.

2. What sets your bees apart from other mason bee vendors?

My basic methods adhere to the recommendations of the best science, namely the work of the USDA Bee Biology & Systematics Lab in Logan, Utah. A working relationship with the lab was part of the foundation of my business. I have modified the USDA protocols to suit my particular operations and local conditions. Specifically, I produce bees in the best quality nesting materials and rear them to maturity under optimal criteria. Every cocoon is individually inspected before sale. I cull outsized, diseased, and parasitized cocoons. I have direct control over all the bees I harvest and sell. Each production batch, corresponding to locality, is sampled for overall health, parasite load, and sex ratio. The customer is guaranteed the exact number of bees ordered (or slightly more), a minimum sex ratio, and healthy, vigorous bees kept cool until received.

3. What have been the biggest challenges for you in rearing the bees, and operating the business? And how have you dealt with these challenges?

More commonly, bees are acquired from commercial sources, either directly from producers (colloquially called "bee ranchers") or from retail sources who buy directly from producers (see sidebar, below).

The blue orchard bee is commonly managed as a backyard orchard pollinator. There are a handful of high-profile producers of the bee located in the Pacific Northwest. It is important to note that while these western producers sell bees nationwide, they are in fact selling the western subspecies of this BOB (*Osmia lignaria propinqua*) outside of its native range. The potential consequences of the western bee hybridizing with its eastern relative, and of parasite and disease movement, are unknown. Emergence timing and winter dormancy of non-local BOB populations may also be less than satisfactory.

While the BOB is distributed across most of the northern US, the eastern subspecies is uncommon in many areas—perhaps due to habitat loss—which is one of the reasons why the Japanese hornfaced mason bee (*Osmia cornifrons*) was imported. Currently, commercial distribution and grower acceptance of the hornfaced bee is not widespread but is growing. Individuals interested in keeping mason bees east of the Rocky Mountains are advised to either trap nest their local native BOB subspecies or to consider using the hornfaced bee.

Purchased mason bees are typically sold in nest

The biggest technical challenge has been dealing with the hairy-fingered mite, *Chaetodactylus krombeini*. This species reaches very high population levels in my region and can be lethal to the bees. I monitored infestation levels and struggled with control methods for years. I have now developed a method, based on the pioneering biological studies of others, of reducing mites to low or even insignificant levels with simple management during the rearing period. I sell only mite-free bees.

The greatest business challenge has been to decide how large and how fast to grow my business. Until the last two years the market has been slow and very "niche"-oriented. Now demand is increasing quickly so it is a safer decision to grow.

4. What are some of the most frequent questions or technical problems you hear from people keeping mason bees?

I don't hear much, to tell the truth, beyond hairy-fingered mite issues. The industry is young, fragmented, and most producers are still pretty naive about professional management. My impression is that this shows up in the varied quality of bees sold. We need to talk more, have a producers meeting, establish a newsletter, start an organization. Our problems are similar in some ways to those in the honey bee industry, and their solutions will, in the same way, require cooperation among various stakeholders.

Perhaps the biggest problem facing the industry is uninformed and unregulated brokerage. Because of the lack of information and the "gold rush" mentality, there is a tendency to broker bees without any quality control. In the short run, this will result in shortchanging customers. In the long run it will result in bad publicity, hamper acceptance of alternative pollinators, and worst of all, exacerbate disease and parasite problems. I advise potential customers, even if I end up not supplying them with bees, to buy direct from reputable producers who can guarantee quality bees.

5. What do you think is needed for broader acceptance/usage of mason bees as pollinators among commercial growers?

More good science and good publicity. Also, setting standards so that customers can know what to expect. We need to get cooperative extension educators on board with good information so they can help educate growers.

In addition to selling bees, Dr. Sugden's company provides bee and pollination related consulting, as well as scientific illustration and writing.

Entomo-Logic
21323 232nd St., SE
Monroe, WA 98272-8982
Phone: (360) 863-8547
http://www.entomologic.com

tubes (usually cardboard or reed) that have been capped with a mud plug. Occasionally no effort is made by producers to inspect the cocoons within those filled tubes, which may contain parasites, diseased bee larvae, poor sex ratios, or even no bees! Ideally, purchased bees should come with some quality assurance and statement of inspection methods. X-ray sampling and loose cocoon examination are common ways in which bee populations are randomly sampled for parasites, diseases, and overall health. Some producers only sell bees as loose cocoons that have been removed from their natal tube. This practice has various advantages and disadvantages (see sidebar, below).

Purchased bees, whether in filled tubes or loose cocoons, will be dormant upon arrival. Prolonged exposure to warm temperatures can result in premature emergence or depletion of energy reserves due to increased metabolic activity—literally resulting in starvation. For this reason, purchased bees are normally only shipped by producers during the winter months. Ideally, dormant bees that are shipped long distances should be mailed in insulated containers containing frozen ice packs. The ice should not be in direct contact with nest tubes or loose cocoons, and care should be taken to prevent damage from condensation or liquid. Upon arrival, dormant bees should remain in cold storage until ready for release.

LOOSE-CELL MANAGEMENT OF MASON BEES

While most mason beekeepers leave the dormant silk-covered cocoons intact within their natal nest tubes, some people choose to remove them prior to placement in cold storage for the winter. This practice, known as *loose-cell management,* is more commonly associated with leafcutter bees (see chapter 7, page 75, for more information).

An advantage of loose-cell management is that individual cocoons can be inspected and treated for parasites or disease. Some beekeepers claim to effectively control heavy chalkbrood or hairy-fingered mite infestations by immersing the loose cocoons in a 5 percent bleach solution for five minutes.

Another advantage of loose cells is that bee ranchers with mixed species (such as blue orchard bees and horn-faced bees) can separate the

Eric Mader

Figure 6.14 Emergence box system: loose cocoons removed from their nest tubes the previous season are placed in a cardboard emergence box with a single exit hole. The dried, mud-like material around the box is the result of bees defecating upon emergence.

various populations by appearance.

Loose-cell management has some significant risks and drawbacks, however. Damage to cocoons is always a significant possibility, both through rough handling and prolonged exposure to bleach treatments. Additionally, loose cocoons are at a much greater risk to parasitism by chalcid wasps, and storage areas must be kept meticulously clean.

Finally, bees emerging from loose cocoons have an extremely high dispersal rate and are often unlikely to nest near their release location. This can be controlled somewhat by inserting female cocoons individually into new nest tubes, or by placing loose cocoons into an emergence box (figure 6.14) with a single exit hole within the field shelter. Even with these efforts, however, results may not be satisfactory.

Table 6.1 provides a management timeline for mason bees in northern states.

Nest Materials

Common materials used as mason bee nests include drilled wooden blocks, reed or bamboo sections, cardboard tubes, and grooved boards (figure 6.15). Historically, the earliest mason bee nests in the US were similar to nest designs for the alfalfa leafcutter bee—consisting of drilled pine or fir boards, usually 6-inch x 6-inch boards up to 4 feet (~15 x 15 centimeters and up to ~1.2 meters) in length. To reduce weathering and water damage, the outer surfaces of these nests are usually treated with polyurethane varnish. Treatment of the inner cavities is not necessary and may actually repel bees.

These solid nest blocks are drilled with a series of dead-end holes for nest tunnels. Nest blocks of this type are commercially available, and are fairly attractive to bees. With these nests, dormant bees are left to overwinter inside the block. The block is either left outside or placed in cold storage.

Because the inner nest surfaces of nest blocks cannot be exposed for cleaning, they tend to become contaminated over time with diseases, such as the fungal pathogen chalkbrood (*Ascosphaera torchioi*), or

Eric Mader

Figure 6.15 Nest options including drilled wooden blocks, grooved boards, and cardboard tubes. The use of paper inserts (such as the one protruding from the cardboard tube), make cocoon inspection and nest cleaning easier.

Table 6.1 Mason Bee Management Timeline for Northern States*	
MONTH	**TASK**
January	Buy or sell any bees or nesting materials. Check for mold growth on stored nests or loose cells.
February	Last month to safely mail dormant bees in most areas.
March	Set up field shelters and nests.
April	Observe crop bloom development. Place dormant bees in the field for natural emergence or incubate at 72° to 84 °F (~22° to 29°C) until the first female bees emerge (maintain emerged male bees in cold storage). Control field predators such as ants and earwigs by greasing the legs of field shelters. Provide an ongoing mud source. Nesting begins!
May	Nesting continues.
June	Nesting ends for BOB and hornfaced bees. Remove nests from field and store in ventilated garage or barn with nest entrances facing up and covered with 1-inch layer of sawdust or vermiculite. Set up light traps for parasite control.
July	Avoid disturbance to nests. Check and refill light trap with water and detergent. Storage temperatures should be mid-70's (°F) (~24°C), unless emergence timing is being manipulated.
August	Avoid disturbance to nests. Continue to maintain light trap for parasites.
September	Check development stage via x-ray analysis. Begin pre-chilling bees by gradually moving the nests to a cooler location (not in cold storage).
October	Disinfect nests and shelters. Begin removal of cells from nests if desired, being sure to cover any loose cells with a 1-inch layer of sawdust or vermiculite.
November	Clean any loose cells; Place bees in cold storage at 35° to 40° F (1.7° to 4.4°C) and 50% relative humidity for the next 100 to 200 days. Control parasites if bees are stored in a nonsecure area. Quantify your bee population.
December	Clean and repair beekeeping equipment.

* Timeline and months may vary by region. Bees in California, the Southwest, or southern states may require a different rearing schedule.

parasites such as the hairy-fingered mites (*Chaetodactylus krombeini*) over time. See Appendix A, page 114, for more information. Nests in continuous use for several seasons tend to be the most contaminated.

In order to remove bees from these nests for cleaning, a phaseout system must be employed. Phaseout systems prevent emerging bees from returning to old nests, thus allowing old nests to be disinfected before reuse. Typically a phaseout system will include an opaque container or some kind of dark emergence box attached to the field shelter. This opaque container should have a small opening through which light can enter. As bees emerge from the nest tunnel, they are attracted to the light and exit into the shelter, which should be furnished with clean, previously unused nests. Then, after all bees have emerged, the old nest blocks can be removed for cleaning. In this way, old nest materials are phased out on an annual basis. Once the nest blocks are empty, they are disinfected by submerging in a bleach-water solution (1:3) for one minute, and then allowed to dry.

An alternative to phaseout systems is the use of paper straw tunnel liners. Such straws are inserted into the nest holes, and then removed several months after the nesting period. The tubes containing dormant bees are then typically placed in a parasite-free storage area for the winter. The nest blocks are cleaned using the 1:3 bleach-water treatment.

If paper tube liners are used in solid blocks, the inserted end should be closed off with wax, hot glue, or something similar to avoid the innermost cocoon becoming attached to the inner wall when the straw is removed. Similarly, straw liners should fit snugly within the cavity to prevent parasitic wasps from entering any vacant spaces between straws and inner walls.

Finally, some solid block nests are drilled all the way through and sealed on one side with some type of backing material such as foil-type duct tape. With this backing removed, nests can be more thoroughly cleaned and inspected before they are reused. The problem with these nests is that, unless the backing material is extremely tight fitting, parasites and nest destroyers such as earwigs can easily move between tunnels. Also, if adhesive-type backings, such as foil duct tape are used, the cavities must be dusted

with sand to cover the exposed sticky surface, and to reduce light reflection (which may repel nesting females). Another option for backing material is a sheet of closed-cell foam held in place by a rigid board. See Appendix E, page 134, for an example.

Aggressive sanitation, annual nest phaseout, the use of paper straws, and removable backing materials will minimize parasite and disease issues, but is unlikely to completely eliminate them. To maintain bee health, nest blocks should be periodically discarded and replaced with new ones.

Grooved boards (also called laminates) are a stackable nesting system consisting of individual boards routed with a series of channels (figure 6.16). When the boards are clamped together, the channels form a series of tunnels similar to a solid nest block. The advantage of laminates is that they are easily disassembled, allowing for thorough cleaning and inspection. However, crevices between boards may allow light to enter, making the nests less attractive to bees. And they also may provide additional access points for parasites. As with solid block nests, paper straw liners can be used with laminated boards. Grooved boards should also be phased out regularly and cleaned following the guidelines for solid block nests (figure 6.17).

Cardboard tubes are another popular nesting option, often used in conjunction with removable paper straw inserts and plastic stoppers. Tubes are cheap and readily available from many manufactur-

Eric Mader

Figure 6.16 This nest consists of a series of grooved boards bound together to form a solid block. Small gaps between boards can allow parasites to enter and discourage nesting. The small size and placement are also less than ideal.

Figure 6.17 *Osmia aglaia* nesting in grooved board nests. This species is being studied in the Pacific Northwest as a berry crop pollinator.

ers. When bundled together, cardboard tubes of the same length present a solid surface of nest tunnels. To provide visual landmarks for returning foragers, they should be painted in varying colors. Nesting females entering the wrong nest cavities result in skirmishes, and the spread of parasites and disease. Cardboard tubes also provide less protection against moisture and predators, and are less attractive to bees than wood surfaces. If cardboard tubes are used, walls should be at least 1 millimeter thick to reduce egg laying by parasitic wasps such as *Monodontomerus* (see Appendix A, page 114). As with solid block and grooved board nests, cardboard tubes should be phased out regularly to prevent re-nesting in previously used cavities.

Finally, cut sections of reed or bamboo may be used as nests. These materials are normally cut in a way that uses the natural node as a tunnel backing—creating either single tubes, or two tubes facing opposite directions separated by a central node. These materials provide the same durability as solid wood blocks, but are lower in cost and more attractive to bees. When bundled together the irregular lengths, diameters, and cut surfaces provide ample navigational cues for returning foragers. The irregular hole sizes and lengths also appeal to the natural

size variation within bee populations—providing nesting sites for larger and smaller individuals. Cost is minimal with bamboo and reed nests. Bamboo garden stakes are readily available from landscape suppliers in various diameters and lengths. Tube sizes that are too large or too small should be discarded. Phragmities reed, which is considered an invasive wetland plant in many areas, can often be collected for free. Both can be cut with small, sharp pruning shears or fine-toothed saws. Care should be taken to reduce rough cut ends that may damage the wings of bees. When phased out regularly, reed and bamboo tubes promote extremely healthy populations. The rigid walls provide good weather resistance and protection from predation and parasitism. The tubes are also easily split using a sharp blade, allowing cocoons to be inspected without damage. The primary disadvantage with reed and bamboo nests is the labor-intensive cutting and sorting process making reed and bamboo nest materials costly to use in large bee ranching operations.

Currently no single nest type is free of problems. It is likely that an optimal nest for small producers may be a hybrid of some of the systems listed above. An ideal nest system should be standardized as much as possible, exclude pathogens and parasites, and increase the number of female bees. For more information on the benefits and drawbacks of various nest types, see Appendix F, page 138.

Preferred Nest Dimensions

For BOBs the preferred internal cavity dimensions are $^{19}\!/_{64}$ inch (7.5 millimeters) in diameter by 6 inches (~152 millimeters) in length. These dimensions are highly attractive to nesting females and result in the highest number of female offspring. Smaller diameters and shorter cavity lengths result in more male offspring and fewer offspring altogether. Larger diameters and longer cavity lengths on the other hand require more effort (for building mud walls, and depositing food provisions) and are less attractive to nesting females.

The hornfaced bee is slightly smaller on average than the BOB and prefers correspondingly smaller nest cavities. Current recommendations among some producers in Japan are for internal diameters between $\frac{7}{32}$ and $\frac{15}{64}$ inch (~5.75 and 6 millimeters), and lengths between $4\frac{23}{32}$ and $5\frac{1}{2}$ inches (~12 and 14 centimeters).

Other *Osmia* species likely prefer other tunnel dimensions based on their physical size, but little published information exists.

In addition to cavity dimensions, inter-hole distances are also an important consideration that influences bee health and the time required for nest provisioning. Nests with flat front surfaces—such as drilled blocks or grooved boards—should have inter-hole distances of ¾ inch (19 millimeters) or even higher. This distance will result in easier orientation for female bees that are returning to the nest from foraging trips. Bees that can easily find their nest hole will complete nests more quickly and are less likely to enter the wrong nest holes where they could become contaminated with disease spores. Many commercially available nests tend to have higher hole densities which can be problematic.

Nests consisting of raised or textured orientation patterns, and irregular surfaces (such as bundles of reed cut in various irregular lengths), result in easier orientation for returning foragers, and in these cases the issue of ¾-inch inter-hole distances can be ignored.

Where nests blocks with flat surfaces are used, the front surface should be painted in alternating geometric patterns to help with orientation. Similarly, if bundles of cardboard straws are used, the openings of random straws should be painted in various colors to assist with navigation. Anecdotal evidence suggests that alternating dark colors such as blue and black are most attractive.

Nest Shelters

Mason bee nests require protection from moisture, wind, and direct summer sunlight. In addition, nest shelters serve as a visual landmark for bees returning from foraging trips. Once installed, shelters and partially filled nests MUST NOT be moved during the nesting season. Any movement will result in disorientation for nesting bees and high numbers of bees drifting to other nesting sites.

A significant amount of research has been performed on field shelters for alfalfa leafcutter bee

AVOIDING PESTICIDE POISONING

As with other bees, mason bees are very sensitive to pesticide use, and spraying should be avoided during the nesting period. Once nest tunnels are plugged, larvae and dormant adults are safe from most agricultural chemicals. For more information on avoiding pesticide toxicity to bees, see Appendix D, page 130.

If pesticides must be applied during the nesting period, bees should be protected by performing spraying applications at night and by securing nests against drift. Nests should not be moved during the nesting period as female bees become disoriented by the slightest change in position of nest tunnels, and developing larvae can easily become dislodged from their food provision.

If nests must be moved, they should be covered with a tight-fitting (non-adhesive), ventilated material at night when the females are within the nest tunnels. Fabric such as burlap is an acceptable covering option. Remember that nests containing larvae should always be handled with the entrance tunnels facing up.

Nests that are removed from the field can be placed in cold storage for three or four days with minimal harm. When nests are returned to the field, they should again be transported at night, and PLACED IN THE EXACT POSITION FROM WHICH THEY WERE REMOVED.

An alternative option is a nest shelter with a tight-fitting door that can be closed overnight prior to spraying and kept closed for up to 24 hours while any residual toxicity outside the shelter dissipates.

None of these options is ideal and any disruption is likely to result in significant dispersal by nesting females.

nests, and the same principles apply to mason bee shelters. The most important of those principles is size. A common mistake that mason beekeepers make is the use of shelters that are too small, or worse, not using any shelter at all (by attaching drilled blocks or bundles of reeds directly onto trees or fence posts) (figure 6.18). Small shelters are difficult for nesting female bees to locate in the landscape. Instead, large profile shelters act like billboards for returning bees. Large shelters also provide basking areas for bees to warm themselves during cold spring mornings before flight and protection from high wind velocities which hamper nesting.

Freestanding leafcutter shelters used in the Canadian provinces are commonly 6 to 10 feet high, by 8 feet wide and 4 feet deep (~1.8 to 3 meters high, by 2.4 meters wide and 1.2 meters deep) (figure 6.19). Commercially produced structures include tent-like shelters with metal frames and fabric sides, as well as molded plastic dome shelters. However, many beekeepers also construct their own plywood shelters. Any of these designs are excellent for mason bees, however slightly smaller designs, as necessary

Eric Mader

Figure 6.18 A small nest hanging from a trellis wire. The cylinder is constructed from a section of PVC pipe. The small size and location are less than ideal, but such nests scattered around an orchard can be useful to capture stragglers who disperse from larger shelters.

Eric Mader

Figure 6.19 A large homemade orchard shelter containing several thousand nest tubes. The steel cage provides protection from birds and rodents, although its use should be avoided if possible. Note the insides of individual buckets are painted blue to make them more attractive to bees.

for orchard conditions, are also acceptable. Shelters deeper than 3 to 4 feet (0.9 to 1.2 meters) remain dark and are less attractive to bees. Regardless of design, freestanding shelters are easily toppled in strong winds unless firmly secured to the ground.

If small shelters are used they should be grouped together to form a landmark, or they should be placed against a barn wall or some other large structure. Conversely an open barn or shed directly adjacent to the field can be used as a shelter with the nests hung inside the building.

Shelters should also be painted in colors that contrast with the landscape. Contrasting light and dark vertical lines or other paint patterns may be helpful visual cues for returning bees.

Since foraging activity increases under high light intensity, shelters should face east or southeast if possible so that they capture sunlight early in the day. Direct sunlight is fine in early spring, but it is not favorable in the summer and can overheat larvae inside finished nests. Temperatures higher than 90°F (32.2°C) can be lethal to developing bee larvae. Similarly shelters that receive direct sunlight in late winter may result in emergence before sufficient forage is available.

The nests can be left in the shelter year-round where the bees will develop and emerge naturally at ambient temperatures. As stated earlier, some type of phaseout system should be employed to prevent bees from re-nesting in previously used nests. Such systems can be incorporated into the shelter design, employing a closed off compartment with a single exit hole. Bees (and parasites) are attracted to light entering the hole and will exit the phaseout chamber into the larger shelter where clean empty nests are installed. After the emergence period ends, the old nests can be removed from the phaseout chamber and cleaned. Shelters left in the field year-round should be loosely attached to ground anchors during the winter months to prevent damage from frost heaving.

Shelters may also need to be secured against predators. Ants and earwigs are a common problem. In freestanding shelters, they can be discouraged by coating the shelter legs with automotive grease. Woodpeckers, barn swallows, other birds, as well as squirrels, can all become a nuisance. Birds can be excluded if necessary using plastic netting with the largest mesh size possible. The netting should be pulled tautly. Metal mesh should not be used as it can damage the bee's wings. Various bird-scare devices may also be sufficient; mesh should only be used as a last resort.

Finally, just because a shelter can accommodate a large number of nests doesn't necessarily mean it should. There is some good evidence to suggest that shelter crowding results in fierce nest tunnel competition which stresses bees. This crowding may also translate into higher levels of chalkbrood disease and parasites. A minimum of two empty nest tunnels per female bee should be provided each season. More is better.

Release Rates, Methods, and End-of-Season Removal

Mason bees have a limited effective foraging range from the nest—probably not much more than 100 yards (~90 meters). At higher distances, bees tend to prefer nest sites closer to the forage source. Depending on the area to be pollinated, multiple shelters scattered throughout the orchard or farm may be needed.

Current USDA Bee Lab recommendations call for stocking rates of 250 female BOBs per acre (~620 per hectare) for apple pollination, and 300 per acre (~740 per hectare) for almonds. Hornfaced bees are likely to be equally effective at these rates. Rates for other *Osmia* species and other crops are not commonly established.

Release of bees maintained in cold storage should be timed to coincide with the beginning of the bloom period. In orchard settings, females that emerge significantly before the first blooming flowers are likely to disperse in search of adequate food sources elsewhere. Early flowering, alternative forage sources are extremely valuable to prevent this. Plants like willow, dandelion, and Siberian squill provide excellent food sources in orchards for BOBs and hornfaced bees before fruit tree bloom.

Similarly, bees released too late in the season may emerge as the main crop bloom is in decline. With-

out alternative forage sources, many bees are likely to disperse in addition to missing the peak pollination period.

Flower bud development and weather forecasts should be monitored prior to placement of bees in the field. Assuming they have had an adequate cold storage period (roughly 100 to 200 days), emergence of male bees can be expected within one day to a week when outdoor temperatures reach the 70s (°F) (~21 to 26°C). Female emergence for BOBs and hornfaced bees typically begins after about half of the male bees have emerged—usually within three to five days of steady warm temperatures. At cooler temperatures, in the 50s or 60s (°F) (~10 to 20°C), emergence will still proceed, but over a longer period of days.

One method of assuring that emergence corresponds to the main crop bloom is to stagger the release of bees. Nests containing dormant bees can be removed from cold storage over several days, placing only half or a third of the nests in the field at a time.

Bees overwintered in the field, or at ambient outdoor temperatures (such as in an unheated barn or garage), will have a variable rate of emergence lasting over several weeks. Bees maintained under such conditions should be winter hardy for that region and have a diversity of forage sources available throughout the nesting period.

Ideally, mason bees should be released from their original nests, employing a phaseout system. Bees forced to chew out of their natal nest have a lower dispersal rate. If loose cocoons are used, they should be released in an emergence box consisting of a dark container with a single exit hole (identical to the phaseout system described earlier). Loose cocoons within the emergence box are at great risk of parasitism by chalcid wasps, and should be covered with an inch of sawdust or vermiculite (not perlite). Emerging bees can readily dig their way out and exit the emergence box, but smaller-bodied parasites have greater difficulty digging down to the loose cocoons.

Active nesting for BOBs and hornfaced bees lasts one to two months depending on weather and forage sources. Near the end of the nesting period few female bees will be visible; those remaining are often slow and have tattered wings. Other cavity nesting bee and wasp species may appear, as well as parasites such as large ichneumonid or smaller chalcid wasps. These parasites signal that it is time to remove nests from the field. At this stage, bees are still in the larval stage, and rough handling of the nests can cause them to be dislodged from their pollen-nectar food provision. Unnecessary jostling should be avoided. Nests removed from the shelter should be stored with the entrances facing up so that larvae remain in contact with their food at all times.

Locally acclimatized populations may be left in field shelters to develop naturally and emerge the following year. However, such populations are at greater risk to predation, parasitism, and overheating.

Storage, Incubation, and Emergence Manipulation

Following nesting, larval development continues within the nest tunnel for several months with pupation occurring in late summer for BOBs and hornfaced bees. Adulthood is reached in autumn with the exact timing dependent upon local conditions. During this process cocoons can be randomly examined by careful dissection or x-ray analysis (see Appendix B, page 126) to monitor growth stage and overall health.

Development occurs rapidly at warmer temperatures compared to lower temperatures. A rearing regime at the USDA Bee Lab in Logan, Utah produced adult bees in 63 days when larva were kept at 84°F (28.9°C). Bees maintained at 64°F (17.8°C) took nearly twice as long, 123 days, to reach adulthood. Developmental temperatures maintained in the mid-70s (°F) (~24°C) are probably close to ideal. Fluctuating temperature regimes with a daily cycle of 8 hours at 57°F (13.9°C) and 16 hours at 81°F (27.2°C) have also been used on BOBs with success.

Faster development generally results in lower larval mortality. However, pre-wintering adults stored at warm temperatures for extended periods maintain high metabolic rates. Such bees may use up their stored fat reserves and literally starve to death during the winter or emerge as weak adults the following spring—often unable to fly or even chew out of the nest. To prevent energy depletion, BOBs and hornfaced bees should be cooled within two to four weeks of reaching adulthood.

Under natural conditions with locally native bees, this is usually not a problem. For example, BOBs can usually be stored outdoors in an unheated, sheltered location over the winter—unless the population was obtained from a significantly different climate.

With non-local bees, artificial rearing conditions are required. Hornfaced bees for example are believed to have less tolerance for subfreezing weather and should be maintained under controlled conditions in most areas.

Winter dormancy, or *diapause*, is required for emergence. The lengthy period of exposure to cold temperature ensures that bees emerge the following spring in synch with blooming plants. For BOBs from most areas of the US, the required length of diapause is normally between 100 to 200 days of cold exposure. Practically speaking, BOBs placed into cold storage in October are normally ready for emergence in April or May the following year. The diapause requirements for hornfaced bees are likely somewhat shorter.

When using artificial cooling, dormant bees should be stored between 35° and 40°F (~1.7° and 4.4°C) at about 50 percent relative humidity. Standard kitchen refrigerators are fine, but they should be used with an indoor/outdoor thermometer (figure 6.20). By placing the outdoor probe inside the refrigerator,

Eric Mader

Figure 6.20 Dormant adult bees in filled nest tubes can be refrigerated over the winter to protect them from temperature extremes and to control spring emergence. The outdoor probe of the digital thermometer is placed inside the refrigerator so you can keep track of the temperature without opening the door.

the internal temperature can be monitored without opening the door. Humidity inside the refrigerator can be maintained at adequate levels by maintaining an open tray or pan filled with water. Rather than placing bees directly into cold storage, they should be gradually cooled over a period of several days.

Wherever dormant bees are stored, it is imperative that the areas be free of rodents. Storage containers should be opened periodically to allow fresh air to enter and to prevent the growth of mold. In non-refrigerated conditions, bees should also be protected from parasites. Common methods include covering nest materials and loose cells with a layer of vermiculite (figure 6.21) or storing inside a nylon stocking. Keep in mind, however, that if your bees are infested with parasites, these measures may prevent parasites from dispersing.

In addition to physical barriers, light traps are an effective tool against some parasites, including the extremely destructive chalcid wasps. Light traps consist of a black light suspended above a pan of water. A small amount of detergent should be added to reduce surface tension. Parasitic wasps and various nest destroyers are attracted to the light where they fall into the pan and drown. Light traps should be placed on the floor of the storage area, as chalcid wasps are poor fliers. Similarly if the storage area is a

Eric Mader

Figure 6.21 After the nesting season, these nest tubes are covered with a layer of vermiculite to protect them from parasites.

Note for figure 6.21: The vermiculite is removed before the nests are place outdoors for emergence the following season. Notice that the tubes are stored with the entrances facing up so that larva are not dislodged from their food source and to prevent them from spinning their cocoons in the wrong direction.

darkened room, a single window can be substituted for the black light. It is imperative that light traps—if they are used in the spring—are secured to prevent accidental drowning of emerging bees. For more information about mason bee parasites and diseases, see Appendix A, page 114.

Manipulation of diapause and emergence is an area of ongoing research. The ability to time bee emergence to peak crop bloom is essential if mason bees are to be maintained as managed pollinators. This is especially critical when using non-local bee populations for crops that bloom very early in the season (such as almonds) or crops that bloom late in the nesting season (such as highbush blueberries).

Close monitoring of bud swell is necessary when determining the need for bees. For most spring blooming orchard crops—such as apples, pears, and cherries—BOBs and hornfaced bees can simply be removed from cold storage one to two weeks before the anticipated bloom with satisfactory results. Emergence will occur over a period of a week or more.

For slightly later spring blooming crops, bees can be safely maintained in cold storage for one to two months longer than the natural emergence period. Extended chilling results in faster emergence, and some male bees may begin appearing in the cooler. Prolonged cold storage will negatively affect bee survival. The upper limit of safe chilling of BOBs and hornfaced bees is probably not more than 220 days. Bees cannot be maintained in cold storage for more than one season.

Advancing natural emergence is often required for very early blooming crops, such as almonds. In these cases bees can be artificially incubated, as is commonly done with alfalfa leafcutter bees.

During incubation, filled nests or loose cells should be placed in clean, ventilated, escape-proof containers. Incubation rooms should be well insulated and have sufficient air circulation to prevent hot or cold spots. Rooms should have adequate shelving to hold boxes containing loose cells or filled nest blocks. Dark rooms are also preferable because they reduce stress on the bees and can be used with light traps for parasites, as described earlier.

Room temperature, 68° to 72°F (20° to 22°C), is often adequate for incubation. However, more rapid emergence can be achieved with slightly warmer temperatures, between 72° to 84°F (22° to 29°C). Temperatures higher than 90°F (32.2°C) can be lethal to developing bees. In addition, relative humidity lower that 70 percent can result in developmental deformities. A normal household humidifier can be used inside the incubator. Light traps to control parasites will also add to the overall humidity.

Under these conditions, the first male bees will emerge within 24 to 48 hours if they have had an adequate chilling period. Female emergence follows several days later.

Incubation containers may employ a "bleed-off system" where bees are removed upon emergence and placed back into cold storage until release. Such systems consist of a dark box with a single exit hole leading to a screened cage. As male bees emerge they are attracted to the light outside of the box and gather inside the cage. The cage is then periodically checked, and accumulated bees are placed back into cold storage at the same temperatures used for winter storage. Cages should be checked several times a day.

When the first female bees begin emerging, the now docile chilled male bees and the remaining nests are transported to the field for release. If the bloom period is delayed by weather, the entire population can safely be placed back into cold storage at this point for up to a week if necessary.

Before release, the chilled bees should be placed back inside the incubation container (or a similar phaseout structure), forcing them to again emerge from a single exit hole—thus replicating natural emergence. Bees released in this way, however, are likely to have a higher dispersal rate than bees emerging directly from their natal nest in the field.

For extremely early advanced emergence, the rate of larval development must be increased so that bees can be placed into cold storage earlier (and thus be incubated earlier the following year). As mentioned earlier, larval development occurs more rapidly at warmer temperatures than lower temperatures.

A rearing regime to advance natural emergence of BOBs by two or three months has been developed by USDA Bee Lab in Logan, Utah. The procedure consists of storing recently constructed nests under a fluctuating temperature regime. A continuous daily cycle of 8 hours at 57°F (13.9°C) and 16 hours at 81°F (27.2°C) produced adult bees at about 70 days (as opposed to nearly 100 days under ambient outdoor temperatures). By advancing adulthood in this way bees are ready for cold storage sooner. Emergence incubation can begin after 150 days of diapause. This population will produce offspring which are also out of synch with local populations and weather conditions. All consecutive progeny will need to be maintained under the same artificial conditions.

Other diapause and emergence manipulation methods may exist, and research in this area is ongoing. Commercial bumble bee producers, for example, manipulate diapause by exposing dormant queens to high concentrations of carbon dioxide gas. This procedure is not widely understood and has not been reported with any *Osmia* species.

Estimating Production

Counting plugged nest holes is a poor way to determine actual bee production. Plugged nests may contain few live larvae, may have diseased or parasitized cocoons, exhibit poor sex ratios, or even contain empty chambers.

To determine the health and size of a population, x-ray analysis (as described in Appendix B, page 126), or nest dissection is necessary. This is another reason why drilled blocks, without paper liners, make poor nests. Grooved boards are the most easily disassembled for inspection. Paper liners in cardboard tubes or solid blocks are easily disassembled, or can be inspected by viewing against a strong light. Reed or bamboo nest tubes can also be inspected by carefully splitting them apart with a sharp knife. To minimize damage, nest inspection should be performed after cocoon spinning in the fall.

With experience, cocoons are easy to sex based on position within the tube and size. Remember that female cells occupy the innermost section of the nest cavity and are larger than male cells. Diseased and parasitized cells are also often easy to identify and usually do not contain spun cocoons.

To determine overall health and sex ratios, collect a number of nests at random. The larger the sample size, the more accurate the sample will be. Record findings including the total number of cocoons, the number of male and female cocoons, the number of empty cells, parasitized and diseased cells, etc.

To calculate percentages of various categories for analysis, multiply the number of cocoons times 100, then divide by the total number of cocoons you found. Here is an example:

168 viable cocoons were counted among the nests that were opened. Of these there were 43 female cocoons. What is the percentage of female bees?

$$\frac{43 \text{ female cocoons} \times 100}{168 \text{ total cocoons}} = 25.6\% \text{ female bees}$$

Despite the best efforts of a mason beekeeper, some nests fail to produce any emerging bees each season. These defective tubes should be carefully dissected at the end of the nesting season to determine the cause for failure. Previously unnoticed parasite or disease problems can often be identified in this way, as can other anomalies such as the presence of parsivoltine species. These defective nests should be opened away from stored bees and nesting sites to reduce the spread of pathogens and parasites.

MASON BEEKEEPING IN JAPAN

In 1981 a rural inn in Fukushima Prefecture's Minami Aizu district was declared a historic preservation site by the Japanese government. The house, which is several hundred years old, still retains the traditional thatch roof made of reed. Within these thick layers of reed matting, thousands of *Osmia cornifrons* can be observed nesting each spring. This phenomenon provides a unique glimpse into Japan's agricultural past, when man and mason bee occupied the same homes.

During that agrarian era, inquisitive farm kids quickly learned that the reeds could be split apart revealing the sweet tasting pollen-nectar provision within. This pollen-nectar mixture resembled *kinako*, a traditional food made of soybean flour and honey, leading to the moniker, "bean-powder bee," or *Mame-ko Bachi*—a name which persists to this day. Active management of the mame-ko bachi (commonly called the Japanese hornfaced bee in the West) as a pollinator did not begin until the latter days of World War II.

Habitat loss and increasing pesticide use greatly reduced the number of wild pollinators in Japan's northern apple growing regions by the early 1940s—leading to dramatic declines in yield. Matsuyama Eikyu, an apple grower in Aomori prefecture, had noticed the mame-ko bachi nesting in the cavities of utility poles and boards near his orchard and wondered if he could propagate the bee by providing additional nesting materials. His success was almost immediate, and following the war Matsuyama was awarded a government grant to further his research. Matsuyama went on to lecture about mason beekeeping at several universities. He was also among the first to recognize some of the fundamental principles of mason beekeeping, such as the importance of providing large visible orientation landmarks for bees—placing nest materials against the sides of buildings, rather than hanging them from trees.

Following on the heels of Matsuyama's success, another apple grower, Takejima Gisuke, further refined nesting technology, making him a leading producer of mason bees. During a seven-year period in the 1950s Takejima produced 15,000 nest tubes, containing nearly 150,000 bees, most of which were distributed to other growers as well as University researchers across Japan. Takejima also founded the Mame-ko Bachi Preservation Group, a cooperative organization dedicated to shared research, nesting technology, and establishing distribution standards.

Active research into rearing practices and parasite control was performed throughout the 1960s and 70s at the Aomori Prefecture's Apple Research Institute, primarily under the direction of Yamada Masashi. Today in Aomori's Itayanagi village a monument stands to the mame-ko bachi, and apple growers gather every May 8th to celebrate "Mame-ko Bachi Appreciation Day," complete with an outdoor festival.

7 The Alfalfa Leafcutter Bee

Eric Mader, *Pollinator Outreach Coordinator, the Xerces Society for Invertebrate Conservation*

The alfalfa leafcutter bee (*Megachile rotundata*) (figure 7.1) is the second oldest managed bee species in US. Like the honey bee, the alfalfa leafcutter bee (sometimes called the alfalfa leafcutting bee) is a nonnative species introduced from Europe and the Middle East. There are various explanations for the bee's introduction in the US. One common theory is that the bees accidentally arrived inside wooden shipping crates imported from the Mediterranean region. The earliest record of the alfalfa leafcutter bee in the US dates from 1937 in Washington, DC.

Theresa Pitts-Singer

Figure 7.1 The alfalfa leafcutter bee (*Megachile rotundata*) pollinating alfalfa.

The Advance and Decline of the US Leafcutter Industry

After introduction, the alfalfa leafcutter bee spread westward to the Pacific coast, in the process becoming established as an important wild pollinator of alfalfa for seed production. By the early 1960s, the leafcutter's value as a pollinator was well recognized, and alfalfa growers in western states had developed various artificial nest systems for rearing large numbers of the bee.

The leafcutter bee was successfully managed, and huge annual population increases were common in the 1960s and 1970s. As populations increased, however, so did new parasites and diseases, particularly a fungal disease called chalkbrood (*Ascosphaera aggregata*). The entrenched production practices of US beekeepers failed to adapt to these challenges, and as a consequence, the leafcutter industry collapsed in the 1980s. Since then, numerous leafcutter beekeepers and equipment manufacturers have gone out of business.

Meanwhile, Canadian producers pioneered new management practices which have kept the alfalfa leafcutter bee in common use. Today Canada has emerged as a major producer of both leafcutter bees and alfalfa seed. Unfortunately many of the Canadian management methods rely heavily on a combination of potent fumigants, pesticides, and disinfectants, many of which are not approved in the US.

With the continued decline of the European honey bee in the US, there is a renewed interest in the alfalfa leafcutter bee—not just to pollinate alfalfa, but also to pollinate crops like blueberries, cranberries, and various vegetables. Unfortunately, there has been little corresponding research into improved management methods for this bee. Suppliers of bees and equipment in the US are also uncommon.

The following recommendations are an attempt to suggest more sustainable management practices with the goal of reviving the alfalfa leafcutter bee as a managed pollinator in the US.

Natural History

The alfalfa leafcutter bee belongs to the family *Megachilidae*. The Latin name refers to the large mandibles (jaws) of the bees in this group. Members of the *Megachilidae* family use their large, scissor-like mandibles to gather pieces of leaf, flower petals, mud, or plant resins for the construction of their nests. The genus, *Megachile*, includes bees that construct nests out of leaf pieces or flower petals—the leafcutter bees. There are about 115 species of leafcutter bees in North America, including both native and nonnative species (see sidebar).

The alfalfa leafcutter bee is smaller than many native leafcutter bees ranging from ¼ to ⅜ inch (6.4 to 10 millimeters). Parallel rows of pollen collecting hairs located on the underside of the female bee's abdomen, called the scopa, are silver or gray in color. Other female leafcutter bee species usually have black, tan, or yellow scopa. Female alfalfa leafcutter bees are larger than male bees, (figure 7.3) with a few gray hairs around the face, and a stinger at the tip of their pointed abdomen. Despite having a stinger, female leafcutters are not aggressive, and rarely

---

In the early 1980s researchers at the USDA-ARS Bee Laboratory in Logan, Utah identified a second leafcutter bee with significant management potential.

Because of its affinity for flowers in the Compositae family, the native *Megachile pugnata* (figure 7.2) was dubbed the "sunflower leafcutter bee." Like the alfalfa leafcutter bee, *M. pugnata* nests gregariously in artificial nest blocks and has similar management requirements. Also like the alfalfa leafcutter, *M. pugnata* produces both single and second generation bees based on similar environmental factors.

Rather than lining nest tubes with leaf pieces like most other leafcutters, the sunflower leafcutter combines mud and leaf parts to form a pulp used to separate cells and plug nest entrances. This habit makes loose-cell management of the bee difficult. Instead closed-cell systems

THE SUNFLOWER LEAFCUTTER BEE

more similar to mason bee management are required. The sunflower leafcutter is also nearly twice as large as the alfalfa leafcutter, and requires correspondingly larger nests. In field trials on hybrid sunflower, *M. pugnata* has demonstrated excellent management potential. For instance, a study of pollination efficiency measured nearly one seed fertilized per second during flower visits by the bee. In comparison, honey bees average much lower at only 0.05 seeds per second!

Unfortunately little research on *Megachile pugnata* has been conducted, and no commercial suppliers exist (although wild populations are available in many areas). As with other bees, there are significant management challenges with the sunflower leafcutter including various parasites and chalkbrood; however, for the right person this bee could spark a whole new industry!

Eric Mader

Figure 7.2 Sunflower leafcutter bee, *Megachile pugnata*. Note the row of yellow scopa on the underside of the abdomen.

Eric Mader

Figure 7.3
Male and female alfalfa leafcutter bees. Note the smaller size, rounded abdomen, and longer antennae of the male (below). Also note the row of gray scopa hairs on the underside of the female's abdomen.

sting, even when handled. The sting is also much less painful than that of a honey bee. As a result beekeepers do not need any special protective equipment when working with leafcutter bees. Male bees have conspicuous green eyes, yellow hairs around the face, slightly longer antennae, and straight, non-tapered abdomens with no scopa or stinger.

All leafcutter bees are solitary, meaning that each female bee independently constructs her own nest, provisions the nest with pollen, and lays eggs. There is no queen, and the bees do not live together as a social unit like honey bees do. Female leafcutters do not interact with other bees or with their own offspring after laying their eggs. Alfalfa leafcutter bees are gregarious, however, meaning that they have a tendency to construct their nests near each other; hence large numbers of bees can be housed in a single structure containing multiple nests. Other leafcutter bee species will nest in manmade nests, however most species are difficult to manage because they are not gregarious. Male leafcutter bees have no role in the construction or the provisioning of nests. Upon their emergence as adults, male leafcutters mate one or more times and may live for several weeks, then die. While they may feed on small amounts of flower nectar to maintain their own energy, male bees do not actively collect pollen and have little value as pollinators.

Life Cycle

In nature, leafcutter bees nest in cavities like tunnels made by wood-boring insects. The absence of abundant and secure nesting sites limits the size of wild populations. Artificial nests can be constructed with blocks of wood or Styrofoam drilled with multiple

holes, bundles of paper straws, or even sections of reed or bamboo to increase their population.

When searching for a suitable nest site, a female bee will repeatedly enter and inspect numerous cavities. Tunnel depth, diameter, and material all influence the appeal of the nests to female bees, as well as the ratio of male to female eggs that she will lay.

After selecting a nest hole, the bee will then fly in a zigzag pattern in front of the nest entrance, memorizing its exact location. During this orientation flight, the bee memorizes adjacent visual landmarks which help her to relocate the nest later. After memorizing the location, the nest cannot be moved without disorienting the bee, often causing her to completely abandon the nest.

After memorizing the tunnel, the bee will then fly off in search of suitable leaf material from which to begin construction. Leafcutter bees prefer soft, flexible leaves for nest construction, such as alfalfa leaves and flower petals, clover, buckwheat, roses, lamb's-quarters, and numerous other plants (figure 7.4). Upon finding a suitable leaf, the bee will cut out a semicircular section from the leaf edge (figure

Eric Mader

Figure 7.4
As the name suggests, leafcutter bees cut leaf pieces with their mandibles (jaws). They use the leaf pieces to construct the inner partitions of their nest.

Eric Mader

Figure 7.5 Circular sections cut from the edges of leaves are a sign of local leafcutter bee populations. Bees tend to prefer certain plant species over others for leaf harvesting. Favored plants include buckwheat, wild grape, bindweed, wild senna, rose, and tartarian honeysuckle (pictured).

7.5) with her scissor-like mandibles, resuming flight at the exact moment she finishes cutting out the leaf section. The bee then flies back to the nest with the leaf section held between her legs (figure 7.6). The leaf section may weigh close to one-fourth the weight of the bee herself.

Back at the nest, the leaf piece is transferred to the mandibles as it is carried to the back of the tunnel. Several other half-circle shaped pieces will then be gathered and placed in the back of the tunnel in overlapping layers, creating a cup-shaped concave cell cemented together with salivary secretions and leaf resins. In commercially available nests, $^{15}/_{64}$ to $\frac{1}{4}$ inch in diameter, (~6 to 6.4 millimeters), roughly 15 leaf pieces are required to construct this initial cell. Within this cell the female bee will deposit a provision of pollen and nectar upon which she will lay an egg. The female will then close off the open end of the cell with two or three additional leaf pieces.

In gathering provisions for the nest, the female bee collects pollen which gets trapped among the hairs covering her body. Periodically while foraging, she will groom herself, transferring pollen from the front of her body backward with her forelegs, to the middle legs, and finally to the hind legs which scrape the pollen onto the scopa—the rows of long stiff hairs on the base of the abdomen that hold the pollen granules during the flight back to the nest. The bee also collects nectar while foraging by sticking

Eric Mader

Figure 7.6 Returning bees carrying cut leaf sections that will be used to line the nest interior.

her tongue into the corolla of flowers and sucking the nectar into her crop, or "honey stomach." Upon returning to the nest the bee will enter headfirst and regurgitate the nectar at the back of the cell. She will then somersault inside the nest if there is sufficient room, or she will back out of the nest, turn around and back in. She then scrapes the pollen from her scopa using her back legs and tamps the pollen-nectar paste into position using the tip of her abdomen (see sidebar, page 79).

A total of 15 to 30 trips may be required to gather the necessary pollen and nectar to provision one cell. Initially the mother bee will collect more pollen than nectar, later increasing the amount of nectar collected until the final ration consists of around two-thirds nectar to one-third pollen. Like the leaf pieces from which she constructs the nest cell, these pollen provisions can weigh almost a quarter of the bee's total body weight. Under warm, clear conditions with unlimited forage, a bee may visit up to 25 flowers a minute and complete a single cell in five hours.

Prior to closing off the cell, the mother bee lays an egg which is inserted into the pollen-nectar paste. After closing this cell, she will then immediately begin construction of a second cell, repeating the process until the entire tunnel is almost filled. Depending on the length of the tunnel, 8 to 12 cells may be constructed in a single cavity. When the tunnel is nearly filled with cells, the bee will then collect 10 to 50 circular pieces of leaf which are deposited individually into the nest entrance. These circular pieces are cemented together forming a solid plug which is flush with the hole entrance (figure 7.9). This plug serves as a barrier against rain, predators, and parasites.

Under favorable conditions a female bee may finish two to four tunnels in her lifetime, with a rough average of around 30 eggs—although 50 or more eggs have been documented in some cases. Of course during this nesting period the bee is exposed to predation by birds, insects, and other animals, inclement weather, pesticides, and a host of other conditions that can halt nesting activities at any moment. Female bees spend the evening inside the nest, face inwards. Under overcast conditions, during rain, or when temperatures drop below 64°F (17.8°C), females will remain inside the nest facing outward, guarding against intrusion by other insects.

Alfalfa has an unusual flower for which the alfalfa leafcutter bee is especially well adapted. Like many other legumes, an alfalfa flower consists of one large "standard" petal, two "wing" petals on the sides of the flower, and two fused bottom petals which are called the keel (for their resemblance to a boat keel).

The keel petals enclose the stamen column under tension. When these fused petals are slightly separated by an insect probing the flower, the column is released, springing forward and slamming into the standard petal. Once released, or "tripped," the sta-

ALFALFA POLLINATION

men column does not return to its former position. Only after tripping can successful pollination occur (figure 7.7).

During tripping, the bee is often struck on the head by the stamen column with a great deal of force, and dusted with pollen in the process (figure 7.8). Honey bees often learn to avoid alfalfa flowers because of this tripping action and seek out easier food sources as a result. The alfalfa leafcutter bee, along with the alkali bee (*Nomia melanderi*), and various wild bees, are less deterred by this tripping action and are the chief pollinators of alfalfa flowers.

In addition to alfalfa, the leafcutter bee has been successfully used as a managed pollinator of canola, cranberries, blueberries, and various vegetable crops such as seed carrots.

Eric Mader

Figure 7.7
The alfalfa flower on the left has been tripped. Note the stamen column which has snapped up against the standard petal. The flowers on the right are not yet tripped.

Theresa Pitts-Singer

Figure 7.8 Close-up view of a leafcutter bee with a newly tripped alfalfa flower.

Eric Mader

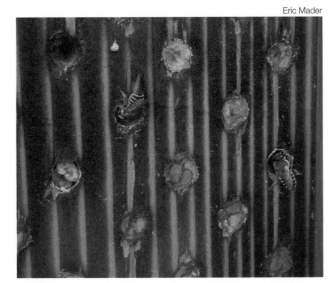

Figure 7.9 After provisioning nest tunnels and laying eggs, leafcutter bees complete the final leaf plugs on the nest entrances.

Mated female bees store sperm in a specialized organ called the spermatheca. The spermatheca allows the mother bee to determine the sex of her offspring by either fertilizing an egg, resulting in a female offspring—or not fertilizing an egg, resulting in a male offspring. Female nest cells are larger and are provisioned with more food. Normally female eggs are laid in the innermost cells, and male eggs are laid in the outermost cells closest to the entrance where parasite and predation rates may be higher because they are more expendable. Sex ratio is determined in large part by the depth and diameter of the nest cavity, with deeper tunnels favoring the production of more female bees. Under optimal conditions, sex ratios should be close to 1.5 to 2 males per female. Many commercially available leafcutter nests favor higher male bee ratios.

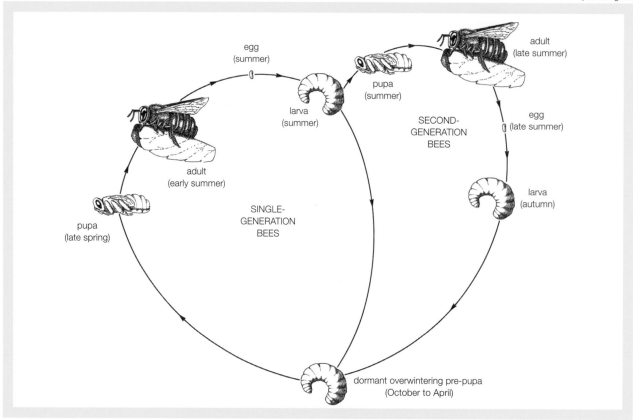

Figure 7.10 Lifecycle of the alfalfa leafcutter bee.

Development time for the bee larvae is temperature dependent (figure 7.10). At 60°F (15.6°C) it takes 15 days for the eggs to hatch and 35 days for the larvae to reach the prepupal stage. At 95°F (35°C) it takes only two or three days for eggs to hatch and eleven days to reach the prepupal stage. The larvae develop through four growth stages called "instars" with rapid increases in size at each stage. High mortality levels can occur during the first or second instar as a result of nest temperatures above 80°F (26.7°C), or from cold periods that prevent feeding. Larvae that die at this stage result in empty pollen-filled cells, called "pollen balls."

In early instars the larva may move around inside its cell; however, the head remains in contact with the food provision. By the fourth instar the larva will have eaten all of the food provision in the cell. It will then defecate and spin a tough silk cocoon produced by its salivary glands. During the cocoon spinning process, the larva will turn completely around inside the cell so that the head ends up facing the nest

entrance. In northern climates, development will then cease, and the bee will overwinter in this dormant prepupal stage. Managed bees are often placed into cold storage at this stage of development and held until the following season.

In northern climates, during the following spring or early summer as temperatures warm, these prepupae again molt into pupae. In southern climates, development may continue uninterrupted resulting in a second generation of bees (see sidebar). In either case, pupae resemble adult bees, except they are completely white in color. Over several days, the eyes of these pupae darken, and the bodies become gray-black in color. Roughly one week after changing color the first male bees emerge by chewing their way out of the nest cells. Male emergence always precedes female emergence, and usually at least 50 percent of all male bees will have emerged prior to the first female appearing.

Mating occurs near the nest from which the bees emerged, with male bees pouncing on the backs of

In northern climates like the prairie provinces of Canada, only one generation of bees is normally produced per season. However, in much of the US, especially in warm years, a significant percentage of the developing bee larvae can fail to diapause (enter dormancy).

This is particularly true of cells which are completed in the early part of the season and can result in emerging adult bees twenty-some days after the time the eggs were laid. In eastern Washington state for example, up to 90 percent of the eggs laid in June may result in second-generation bees. Of eggs laid after mid-July, only 50 percent may develop into second-generation bees, and of eggs laid in August, few second-generation bees will normally emerge.

Second-generation bees are a problem in leafcutter production for several reasons. First, second-generation bees often have less available forage, produce fewer cells, and their larvae must develop late in the season—often under conditions which are too cold for the larvae to feed.

The other problem with second-generation bees is a larger incidence of chalkbrood mortality. As second-generation bees emerge directly from the nest, they chew through any chalkbrood-contaminated cadavers and become covered with chalkbrood spores in the process. These second-generation bees then return to nest and contaminate any new cells they produce.

There have been attempts to control second-generation bees through breeding programs that select for lines of bees that produce only one generation of bees per year. These programs used leafcutter bees imported from southern Europe, and were highly successful. Unfortunately these breeding programs have not been well supported and there is little continuing research into breeding or maintaining these lines of bees.

Limited control of second-generation bees can be achieved by the producer through a variety of practices. Among these is delayed incubation whenever possible to result in later-emerging bees. In addition, nests should be monitored closely and removed from the field when more than 75 percent of the tunnels are capped. These nests should be maintained at around 70°F (~21°C) for about 15 days to allow larvae to finish feeding and develop into the prepupal stage. The nests should then be gradually cooled in a walk-in cooler or air conditioned location to simulate the approach of winter.

newly emerged females. If the female bee is receptive, she will raise the tip of her abdomen and invert her stinger, allowing coupling. Mating lasts less than a minute, and female bees normally only mate once, although male bees may mate repeatedly. Sperm is retained in the spermatheca while the ovaries mature. Within one to two days, the female is ready to lay eggs. During this period she will feed on nectar and find and orient to a suitable nest tunnel.

Female bees prefer to nest near sites from which they themselves emerged, although not necessarily in the same cavity. Following mating some female bees will abscond from the area, in a process referred to as pre-nesting dispersal. As a general rule, the more appealing the nest site, the fewer females will disperse prior to nesting.

Obtaining and Handling Bees

Leafcutter bees can be obtained by trap-nesting wild populations. To do this, nests are set out in the early spring in locations that have good numbers of wild bees, then the nests are removed in the fall. Ideal locations to place nests are on the sides of old barns or wooden farm structures, adjacent to cliff faces or other large visual landmarks, and near ungrazed pasture with sufficient flowers to support wild populations of bees. Nests can be hung inside of open sheds and garages or on south and east facing walls. In all cases, bee nests should be shielded from rain and direct sunlight.

Some individuals have successfully captured good populations of bees on western Bureau of Land Management (BLM) land. (BLM is part of the US

Department of the Interior.) In the past, individuals have operated small businesses out of midwestern trap lines—with nests hung on the sides of barns at numerous farms, then collected and trucked to western states for alfalfa pollination the following year.

Theft of bee nests can be a problem, particularly in western states like Idaho that have an established history of leafcutter production. Bee nests in wild areas should be camouflaged, and marked with the owner's name or symbol. Styrofoam nests are sometimes spray painted, and wooden nests have been marked with hot branding irons.

More commonly, bees are acquired as loose cells (figure 7.11) from Canadian producers, forage seed dealers, or "bee brokers." At the time of this writing

Theresa Pitts-Singer

Figure 7.11 Dormant leafcutter bees are often stored in bulk as loose leaf-covered prepupae.

ESTIMATING PRODUCTION: COCOON SAMPLING AND CERTIFICATION

Counting plugged nest holes, or loose cells, is a poor way to estimate actual bee production. Plugged nests may contain few live larvae, or even empty chambers. Similarly, loose cells many contain chalkbrood-infested larvae, or no larvae at all (pollen balls).

Several public and private agencies in the US and Canada offer professional sampling and certification services that can provide estimates of the number of viable larvae by weight. These estimates can help determine the number of parasitized and diseased larvae, sex ratios, the number of second-generation bees, and the number of cells damaged by mechanical processing, among other things.

Professional laboratories typically sample cocoons through X-ray analysis, although it is possible to do this yourself with the cooperation of a friendly vet-

erinarian. See *Appendix B. X-Ray Procedures for Cavity-Nesting Bees*, page 126, for more information. In addition, labs may perform emergence tests that give an actual total of viable bees in a given sample. When purchasing bees from a commercial broker, they should be accompanied by a certification or analysis worksheet that details the results from these tests (figure 7.12). If you are submitting samples for analysis, contact the lab for specific instructions.

Producers can also sample their own cocoons and bees, although results are likely to be less accurate than professional laboratory results. One simple method is to collect a number of cells at random. The larger your sample size, the more accurate your sample will be. A minimum of 100 cells should be sampled. For solid boards, cells can be removed by constructing a corkscrew-shaped wire probe and gently threading it inside the nest hole between the cells and the inside wall of the nest. This can be very difficult to do!

After collecting several cells, carefully cut the cap off the cell with a sharp penknife or razor blade. Cut into the cocoon, but try not to cut through the larva itself. If necessary examine the inside of the cocoon with a hand lens or dissecting microscope. The cell should contain a single white larva. If there are multiple white larvae inside, the cell has been parasitized by chalcid wasps. If the larva is gray or black there are few brokers of leafcutter bees in the US; often these brokers are not interested in selling small quantities of bees. Loose cells are normally stored in feed sacks and sold by the gallon. A gallon of loose cells may not be an actual gallon by volume, but rather is a measurement designating a quantity of approximately 10,000 dormant bees. The availability of Canadian produced bees varies from year to year and consequently the price also varies. During the past decade, the cost of Canadian produced bees has ranged from $25 to $100 per gallon.

The advantage of these loose cells is that they are normally certified by a regulatory agency which samples the bees for parasites and diseases. See the sidebar (below) on bee certification for more information.

Unlike honey bees, no import permit is required to have leafcutter bees shipped from Canada at the time of this writing. Unfortunately customs officials have trouble understanding this and shipments of leafcutter bees can be held up at the border indefinitely—often under improper storage conditions. Anyone interested in importing bees from Canada should contact the USDA Animal and Plant Health Inspection Service for more information, *and* be prepared to physically bring the bees across the border themselves.

When the loose cells are received, they should be stored between 35° and 40°F (1.7° and 4.4°C) in a cool, dry location (50 percent relative humidity). It is imperative that storage areas be free of rodents.

Northstar Leafcutters

Northstar Seed Ltd. Neepawa, Manitoba, Canada

phone: (204) 476-5241   fax: (204) 476-3773

Leafcutter Bee Larvae Analysis Worksheet

lot # or ID	RR-1			date	Feb. 23/06				
grower									
sub-samples				50 grams sampled					
sample #	good cells	2nd gen	moldy cells	parasit-ized	dead cells	pollen balls	mach dam	total	sub-sample weight (g)
1	87	0	0	0	3	17	2	109	10
2	86	0	0	0	1	22	2	111	10
3	82	2	2	0	1	25	0	112	10
4	94	1	0	0	2	13	1	111	10
5	92	2	0	0	0	13	0	107	10
6									
TOTAL	441	5	2	0	7	90	5	550	50
% total	80.2%	0.9%	0.4%	0.0%	1.3%	16.4%	0.9%	100.0%	
live cocoons/lb.		4004							
							10,000 live bees/gallon		
net weight of bees =									
live bees this lot =									
							24.97 lbs./10 gallons		
20 gallons this lot									

and appears dusty or brittle, it is likely infected with chalkbrood. Record your findings.

To calculate percentages of various categories for analysis, multiply the number of larvae times 100, then divide by the number of cells you examined.

Here is an example:

352 cells were opened. Of these, 78 contained chalcid wasp larvae. What percentage was parasitized by chalcids?

$$\frac{78 \text{ parasitized larvae} \times 100}{352 \text{ opened cells}} = 22\% \text{ parasitized larvae}$$

Labs offering cell analysis:

Montana Department of Agriculture
Alfalfa Seed Committee
http://agr.mt.gov/dept/alfseedCom.asp

University of Idaho
Southwest Idaho Research and Extension Center
http://www.ag.uidaho.edu/parma/

Figure 7.12 Commercial bee brokers should sample bees for parasites, pollen balls, and other problems. Sampling data is often provided to buyers in a written report such as this one.

If the loose cells are stored in plastic or an air-tight container, the container should be opened periodically to allow fresh air to enter, and to prevent the growth of mold. Table 7.1, below, provides a time line for leafcutter management in northern states.

Table 7.1
Leafcutter Management Timeline for Alfalfa Pollination in Northern States*

MONTH	TASK
January	Buy or sell any bees or nesting materials; check for mold growth on stored nests or loose cells.
February	Last month to safely mail dormant bees in most areas.
March	Make a final check of equipment. Test check bee viability if desired.
April	Set up field shelters. Set up incubation room with appropriate equipment: heat source, fans, humidifier, light traps (for parasite control), incubation trays. Or, place nests in field for natural seasonal emergence.
May	Secure nest shelters against field predators such as ants and earwigs by greasing the legs of field shelters.
June	Begin incubation to coincide with crop bloom (refer to incubation timeline). Control parasites with light traps and daily vacuuming.
July	Release incubated bees. Nesting begins! Remove leaf debris from emerging cells as possible. Check field shelters for bats, yellow jackets, and paper wasps.
August	Second generation bees emerge.
September	Remove nests from field. Begin pre-chilling bees by gradually moving the nests to a cool location (not in cold storage).
October	Begin removal of cells from nests if desired, being sure to cover any loose cells with a 1-inch layer of sawdust or vermiculite. Disinfect nests and shelters. Quantify your bee population.
November	Clean and tumble any loose cells. Place bees in cold storage at 35° to 40°F (1.7° to 4.4°C), 50% relative humidity for 150 to 210 days. Control parasites if bees are stored in a nonsecure area.
December	Clean and repair beekeeping equipment. Submit bee samples for lab analysis.

* Timeline and months may vary by region. Bees in California, the Southwest, or southern states may require a different rearing schedule.

Nesting Equipment

Historically leafcutter bee nests consisted of drilled pine or fir boards, usually 3 to 4 inches by 4 to 6 inches (~7.6 to 10 centimeters by 10 to 15 centimeters) in width, and often up to 4 feet (~1.2 meters) in length. Boards were drilled with a series of dead-end holes for nest tunnels. Such nests were extremely attractive to bees and convenient because the bees could be stored and incubated within the boards (figure 7.13).

However, because the inner nest surfaces could not be exposed for cleaning, and because the boards were continually filled with bee larvae, these nests became contaminated with a fungal disease called chalkbrood (*Ascosphaera aggregata*). By the 1980s US beekeepers who continued to manage bees in solid boards saw significant annual losses. To reduce the spread of chalkbrood spores, beekeepers began phasing out solid boards on an annual basis, drilling out the tunnels to remove dead bees and leaf debris. This labor-intensive practice resulted in the term *re-drill* in reference to solid wood nest boards.

While re-drills were the standard American nest for many years, Canadian leafcutter producers pioneered new nest designs that facilitated the annual removal of cells from the nest. Among these nest designs were solid wood blocks that were drilled completely through, and grooved boards (often called

Eric Mader

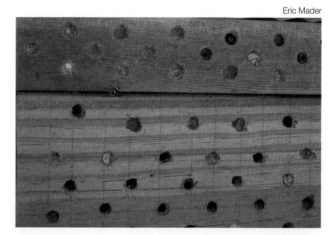

Figure 7.13 Leafcutter bees were historically managed in solid wood blocks drilled with nest tunnels. Because these types of nest cannot be effectively cleaned, they often become contaminated with parasites and diseases over time, causing a decline in populations.

Figure 7.15 Under optimal conditions, these Styrofoam nest blocks are rapidly filled. The open nest holes are the result of second-generation bees which have recently emerged. See sidebar, Second-Generation Bees (page 81).

Figure 7.14 Grooved wooden boards used to be a popular nest option. However boards warp and crack over time and the spaces between boards provide entry points for parasites.

laminates) that consisted of a series of channels routed into the boards, which were stacked together to form a series of tunnels (figure 7.14). These nest types were originally constructed of wood; however, today they are only commonly available as Styrofoam with fabric or foam backing material which is held in place by a series of sheet metal clamps or elastic straps (figure 7.15).

These loose-cell nests have a tremendous advantage because they can be completely disassembled and cleaned each season. In addition, the loose cells require significantly less space for cold storage and incubation than solid boards filled with bees. There are several disadvantages with loose-cell nests, including the potential for greater parasite problems due to the less secure backing material and the poor durability of Styrofoam nests.

Various other nest materials have been used for leafcutter bees, including paper straws and fluted cardboard consisting of a series of tunnel corrugations affixed to a single sheet of paper backing, which is then coiled onto itself forming a round spiral of tunnels. Like the loose-cell nests described above, these paper and cardboard nest materials are much more prone to infestation by parasites than solid wood blocks.

A significant amount of research has been performed on the nesting preferences of leafcutter bees. Tunnel diameter, depth, material, color, and hole density have all been explored, and in many cases the results have been contradictory or inconclusive. General guidelines are as follows: tunnels should be between $^{15}/_{64}$ and ¼ inch in diameter (6 to 6.4 millimeters), and 3 inches to 6 inches in depth (7.6 to 15 centimeters). Nest surfaces should be dark in color, with anecdotal evidence suggesting that blue and black colors are most attractive.

Nest dimensions should be configured to promote bee health and maximize female production, as well as facilitate ease of orientation for foragers returning to the nest. Larger (¼ inch, 6.4 millimeters) and deeper (4 to 6 inches, 100 to 150 millimeters) holes should be used when possible as they encourage larger, healthier brood as well as a higher proportion of female offspring. Inter-hole distances of ⅜ inch (9.5 millimeters), or even higher, will result in easier orientation for female bees that are returning to the nest from foraging trips. Bees that can easily find their nest hole will complete nests more quickly, and are less likely to enter the wrong nest holes where they could become contaminated with disease spores. Commercially available Styrofoam nests tend to have very high hole densities. Similarly, nests with painted, raised or textured orientation patterns, and irregular surfaces (such as wood), all result in easier orientation for returning foragers.

Currently no single nest type is free of problems, and there is much room for experimentation. It is likely that an optimal nest for small producers may be a hybrid of some of the systems listed above—a solid block with removable inserts for example (see Appendix E, page 134). Such a system would no doubt greatly increase labor, but would probably result in a higher percentage of healthy female bees. For more information on the benefits and drawbacks of loose-cell verses solid-board nests, see Appendix F, page 138.

Field Shelters

Bee nests are normally housed in field shelters for protection from rain, wind, and direct sunlight (figure 7.16). As with nests, a great deal of research has been performed on various shelter designs, evaluating them on the basis of heat buildup, wind turbulence, and bee orientation among other factors. Like nests, the results of this research have sometimes been contradictory or inconclusive. One consistent factor has been identified, however: larger shelters provide a better orientation "landmark" for forag-

Eric Mader

Figure 7.16 A simple homemade shelter holding a series of nest blocks. The plywood body is supported by metal fence posts which are driven into the ground.

Theresa Pitts-Singer

Figure 7.17 A simple shelter design using dimensional lumber, plywood, and corrugated metal.

ing bees than do small shelters. Freestanding leafcutter shelters used in the Canadian provinces are commonly 6 to 10 feet high, by 8 feet wide, and 4 feet deep (~1.8 to 3 meters high by 2.4 meters wide and 1.2 meters deep) (figure 7.17). Deeper shelter designs are less attractive to bees especially if darker. Similarly, shelters should be painted in colors that contrast with the landscape. Contrasting vertical lines or other paint patterns may be helpful visual cues for returning bees.

If small shelters are used, they should be grouped together to form a landmark, or they should be placed against a barn wall or some other large structure. Conversely, an open barn or shed directly adjacent to the field can be used as a shelter with the nests hung inside the building.

Commercially produced leafcutter shelters are available from several Canadian manufacturers. These include tent-like shelters with metal frames and fabric sides, as well as molded plastic dome shelters (figure 7.18). Many beekeepers construct their own plywood shelters as well, including elaborate mobile trailer-shelters that can be towed to and from the field.

Since foraging activity increases under high light intensity, shelters should face east or southeast if possible so that they capture sunlight early in the day. Direct sunlight, however, is not favorable and can result in overheating larvae inside finished nests. Similarly, shelters should also be sufficiently open on one side to allow for adequate air circulation, or they should be vented on top to prevent overheat-

Figure 7.18
Manufactured bee shelters are available in tent-like fiberglass and molded plastic versions.

ing. Temperatures higher than 90°F (32.2°C) can be lethal to developing bee larvae. Some producers allow loose cells to finish incubating in the field within the shelter. Beekeepers who do this often paint the roof of the shelter black to collect warmth, and hang the incubation trays just below the ceiling. Again care should be taken to prevent overheating.

Beekeepers that prefer to manage dormant bees inside nest blocks rather than as loose cells can leave the nests in the shelter year-round where the bees will develop and emerge naturally at ambient temperatures. However, if this is done, some sort of phase-out system should be employed to prevent bees from re-nesting in previously used nests. Such systems normally consist of a dark room or box within the shelter with a single exit hole. Bees (and parasites) are attracted to light entering the hole and will exit the phaseout chamber into the larger shelter where clean empty nests are installed. After the emergence period ends, the old nests can be removed from the phaseout chamber and cleaned. Shelters left in the field year-round should be loosely attached to ground anchors during the winter months to prevent damage from frost heaving.

Shelters may also need to be secured against predators. Ants and earwigs may be a common problem in leafcutter shelters. In freestanding shelters, they can be discouraged by coating the shelter legs with automotive grease. Woodpeckers, barn swallows, and other birds can become a nuisance in leafcutter operations. Birds can be excluded if necessary using plastic netting with the largest mesh size possible.

The netting should be pulled tautly. Metal mesh should not be used as it can damage the bee's wings. Since bees passing through netting often bump the mesh, causing them to drop leaf pieces during nest construction, netting should only be used as a last resort.

Wind can cause problems around bee shelters. Excessive wind turbulence around shelters can cause bees to drop leaf pieces as they approach the shelter. To combat this, some shelter designs feature walls extending out from the sides of the shelter, or vertical extensions above the shelter. These features also greatly increase wind resistance, and any shelter, with these extensions or not, should be firmly secured to the ground by attaching the legs to anchored metal fence posts. Guy wires may also be necessary.

Shelters and partially filled nests should not be moved during the nesting season. Any movement will result in disorientation for nesting bees and high numbers of bees drifting to other nesting sites.

There is some debate among beekeepers as to how many bees should be maintained per shelter and how many shelters are needed per field. Of course the final numbers are dependent on the particular crop, but leafcutter bees have a limited effective foraging range from the nest—probably not much more than 100 yards (~90 meters). At higher distances, bees tend to prefer nest sites closer to the forage source. Depending on the size of field to be pollinated, you may need to adjust the number and placement of shelters accordingly.

Finally, just because a shelter can accommodate a large number of nests doesn't necessarily mean it should. There is some good evidence to suggest that shelter crowding results in fierce nest tunnel competition which stresses bees. This crowding may also translate into higher levels of chalkbrood and parasites. A minimum of two empty nest tunnels per female bee should be provided each season. More is better.

Release Rates, Methods, and End-of-Season Nest Removal

Release rates for bees vary between 10,000 (1 gallon) per acre and 20,000 (2 gallons) per acre (~25,000 and 50,000 bees per hectare) for newly seeded alfalfa fields and up to 30,000 to 40,000 bees per acre

(~74,000 to 100,000 per hectare) for established alfalfa fields. At higher rates, more effective pollination occurs, but bee population increases are lower. It is estimated that individual bees can pollinate enough alfalfa flowers to produce ¼ pound of seed (~113 grams). Also remember that under normal production practices, for every female bee there will be 1.5 to 2 male bees. Thus 20,000 bees may contain only 7,000 pollinating females.

There are currently few established release rates for other crops. However, canola growers have been stocking leafcutters at rates of around 20,000 bees per acre (~50,000 bees per hectare), as have blueberry growers in Maine and the Maritime Provinces. This release rate is probably also sufficient for other dense blooms like cranberries, oil and forage crops like clover, vetch, and sunflower, as well as herbs like mint. Less dense blooms would probably achieve adequate pollination at lower stocking rates.

Release methods for bees depend on the nest system used, the crop to be pollinated, and whether or not the bees were incubated. In standard loose-cell management systems for alfalfa pollination, the incubation trays are typically brought to the field on the 22nd day of incubation (or when 30 to 50 percent of female bees have emerged). The trays are placed inside the field shelters, often on shelves suspended from the ceiling inside the shelter.

Elaborate shelters may feature roofs that are painted black to absorb heat, which is radiated below, thus incubating the remaining loose cells. However, care should be taken to prevent excess heat, which can be lethal to developing bees. During transport to the field, trays should be loosely covered with a tarp to calm the bees and prevent wing damage caused by the bees flying against the screened lids.

In cooler climates, incubation trays are sometimes removed from the field shelters at night and returned to a room incubator. The trays are then brought back to the field shelters each morning for the duration of the emergence period. While this practice results in more even emergence, it may interfere with mating, as male bees disperse from the field shelter prior to female emergence.

Bees released as loose cells are likely to have significantly higher pre-nesting dispersal—especially under windy conditions. Therefore the trays should

ideally be transferred to the field on days with fair weather in the morning or early evening when flight activity is reduced. Emerging bees are then more likely to orient to the shelter, rather than dispersing. It is also crucial that the incubation trays are protected from rain so that cells do not become flooded with water.

After emergence is complete, any remaining cocoons and debris in the incubation trays should be burned or buried to reduce the spread of disease. Incubation trays should also be cleaned with a bleach and water (1:3 ratio by volume) prior to re-use.

For bees allowed to develop inside nests, either under incubation or ambient field temperatures, a phaseout system, such as that described earlier, must be employed. Then, after all bees have emerged, the old nest blocks can be removed for cleaning. In this way old nest materials are phased out on an annual basis.

Loose-Cell Processing Equipment

Processing loose cells requires several pieces of specialized equipment. "Cell strippers" are machines used to punch cells from nest blocks, and tumblers break apart the individual cells and remove parasites and debris (figure 7.19). Dip tanks are used to hold strong bleach solutions for disinfecting nests. The scale and level of sophistication varies between producers from

Theresa Pitts-Singer

Figure 7.19 Automated cell harvesters use a series of plunger rods to punch out bee cells from Styrofoam nest blocks into a collection unit below. This particular model incorporates cell tumbling and separates excess leaf litter from the cocoons which are ejected into the garbage can at the right.

small, hand-operated devices, to large automated systems that can process hundreds of thousands of cells per hour. Unfortunately, due to the small number of leafcutter beekeepers, there are few commercial suppliers of processing equipment, the equipment is not cheap, and often machines will only function with one type of nest. As a result much of this equipment is homemade or custom fabricated.

Solid-block cell strippers remove cells from nest blocks using a series of plunger rods that are depressed into the nest tunnels. As the cells are ejected out the back of the nest block they fall through a chute into a collection bin. Manually operated solid-block strippers often have a hydraulic lever which, when pulled down, automatically lifts the plunger rods while the operator repositions the next block.

Grooved-board nest strippers separate the individual nest boards and feed them through a series of blunt teeth. As the teeth scrape across the board, cells fall into a collection bin, and the boards slide into a chute where they are restacked. Manual grooved-board strippers require the operator to carefully pry each board apart and push it past the teeth.

Cell tumblers are used to remove dust, excess leaf pieces, parasites, and debris, as well as to break up individual cells for easier storage. A typical tumbler will consist of a screened drum with a $3/16$-inch mesh (4.8 millimeters). The drum is hand cranked or rotated by an electric motor, allowing the debris to fall through the screen. Sophisticated tumblers will incorporate blowers to remove dust, and will feed the processed cells directly into storage containers or incubation trays. Because of the large amounts of dust produced, cells should be tumbled outdoors, or with proper respiratory protection (see sidebar).

Care should be taken to prevent over-tumbling the cells resulting in the removal of too much leaf material and the exposure of prepupae. When tumbling, maintain a low speed so that cells do not ride up past the sides of the tumbler.

After cell removal, nests should be disinfected in a dip tank containing a bleach and water solution (1:3 by volume) for five minutes. Automated "paddle-wheel" type dip tanks are available that can disinfect a series of nest blocks at one time. Wood nest blocks can also be heat sterilized with steam or in small lumber kilns, although success can be limited.

In addition to disinfecting nests, some beekeepers decontaminate the cells themselves by submerging them in a bleach and water solution (1:3 by volume) for one minute. There is some debate among researchers and producers as to the merit of this practice, and there is a significant potential for harming the larvae if mistakes are made. Based on current information, this practice is probably only of value as a last resort in bee populations with high levels of chalkbrood.

For beekeepers who do not want to process their own loose cells, several bee brokers provide custom stripping and nest cleaning services.

Storage, Incubation, and Emergence

Filled nest blocks can be stored in field shelters or in an unheated building. Bees allowed to overwinter this way under ambient temperatures will typically begin emerging from the nests in early to mid-June and have an extended emergence period that lasts weeks or even months. If the nest blocks are left in field shelters, the shelters must be secured against woodpeckers and rodents with hardware cloth or something similar. Cold weather does not normally injure bees in most parts of the US, and bees can withstand temperatures as low as 15°F (-9.4°C) for short periods of time with little mortality. Exposure to extended periods of freezing temperatures should be avoided. Conversely, warm winter temperatures should also be avoided as some nest-destroying insect pests and parasites may be active at temperatures above 40°F (4.4°C). Filled nest blocks can also be refrigerated; however, few producers have the facilities to store many large nest blocks under climate controlled conditions. During development, either at ambient temperatures or in the incubator, some larvae may spin their cocoons facing the wrong direction. When these bees emerge they then attempt to exit the nest in the wrong direction (toward the back of the nest), possibly killing themselves and other bees in their path. Therefore, if bees are left in nest blocks, the nest blocks should be stored with the tunnel entrances facing up. Bees stored in this way use gravity to determine which way to spin their cocoon, and ultimately exit the nest properly.

More commonly, bees are removed from the nest blocks and stored as loose cells under refrigerated conditions. Feed sacks, buckets, and 50-gallon drums with holes for air circulation are all commonly used to store loose cells. Plastic bags or other airtight containers should be avoided because mold buildup can be lethal to larvae. Cells should also be thoroughly dried before being refrigerated.

Large producers often have walk-in coolers or refrigerated semi trailers that double as incubation rooms. In some areas, seed companies and warehouses also provide cold storage for a fee. Storage temperatures between 35° and 40°F (1.7° and 4.4°C) at 50 percent relative humidity are ideal for both loose cells and filled nest blocks Ordinary home air conditioners are not suitable for maintaining these temperatures—professional refrigeration systems are required. Bees may remain dormant at temperatures up to around 60°F (15.6°C); however, mortality may rise as bees metabolize stored energy reserves at these higher temperatures. Similarly, bees stored at warmer temperatures take significantly longer to emerge. A storage period of 150 to 210 days at 35°F (1.7°C) is probably close to ideal. Dormant bees cannot be stored for more than one season.

The advantages of cold storage and incubation are that pest activity can be arrested, storage space is reduced, and nest blocks can be cleaned and disinfected while the bees are dormant. By combining controlled refrigeration and incubation, bee emergence can be timed to match the onset of peak bloom periods.

Incubation rooms should be well insulated and have sufficient air circulation to prevent hot or cold spots. Rooms should have adequate shelving to hold trays containing loose cells or filled nest blocks. Dark rooms are also preferable as they increase the effectiveness of light traps for parasites, and reduce stress on the bees.

Thermostatically controlled electric space heaters (figure 7.20) and properly vented fuel-burning heaters can be used.

Whatever type of heat source is used, fans should also be used to achieve a consistent temperature throughout the room. Elaborate rooms used for both cold storage and incubation will include separate heating and cooling thermostats and programmable Sensaphone-type room alarms to monitor temperature and humidity inside the incubator. These room alarms normally have an automatic telephone dialer that will contact you if temperature or humidity levels rise or fall outside of established parameters.

Eric Mader

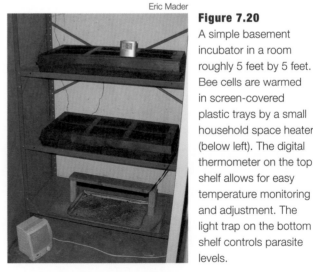

Figure 7.20
A simple basement incubator in a room roughly 5 feet by 5 feet. Bee cells are warmed in screen-covered plastic trays by a small household space heater (below left). The digital thermometer on the top shelf allows for easy temperature monitoring and adjustment. The light trap on the bottom shelf controls parasite levels.

Bees should be placed in sterilized wood, plastic, or Styrofoam incubation trays with tight-fitting screened tops if they are being incubated as loose cells. Since bees give off heat during the development process, incubation trays should not be filled to a depth greater than one inch to prevent cells in the middle of the tray from overheating. A space should be maintained between stacked trays to allow for air circulation.

Incubation should occur at 85°F (29.4°C). Temperatures higher than 90°F (32.2°C) can be lethal to developing bees. Relative humidity lower than 70 percent can result in developmental deformities. A normal household humidifier can be used inside the incubator. Light traps to control parasites will also add to the overall humidity.

Under the controlled conditions recommended here, the first male bees will emerge around 18 days into the incubation, with the first female bees emerging around two days later. If release conditions are unfavorable (cool, wet weather, pesticide spraying, or delayed bloom), bee emergence can be delayed up to one week by reducing the temperature to 65°F (18.3°C) on the 14th day of incubation (see sidebar).

Upon emergence bees should be fed twice daily inside the incubation trays until release with a honey-water solution (1:1 ratio) sprayed onto paper towels and laid across the screened tops of the trays. Since bees extend their tongues through the screen to feed, you should not rub your hands or the paper towels across the screen since this can injure the bees. By the 22nd day, the trays should be taken to the field for release.

Some large producers use a different incubation method called a "bleed-off system." In these systems bees are incubated in open trays in completely dark rooms. As the bees emerge, they are attracted to a single black light placed in a room either adjacent to, or more commonly below, the incubation room. Funnel-shaped chutes guide the bees into storage containers filled with packing excelsior (to prevent the bees from smothering each other) located inside a room which is chilled to 50°F (10°C). The bees remain immobile at these temperatures and can be held for several days. They are then periodically collected and released in the field.

INCUBATION CALENDAR

At 85°F (~29°C) and 70% relative humidity

Day 1. First day of incubation. Bees are in the white grub-like, prepupal form.

Day 7. Canadian producers add Vapona™ (dichlorvos) strips at a rate of ¾ strip per 1,000 cubic feet (28.3 cubic meters) to the incubator at this time.

Day 8 to 9. Larvae begin changing into pupae, still white in color. Bees are extremely sensitive to temperature fluctuations at this time and should not be cooled.

Day 8 to 10. Tiny parasitic *Tetrastichus* and *Ptermomalus* wasps begin emerging. Pupae should be white with pink eyes.

Day 13. Canadian producers remove dichlorovos strips and aerate the incubator with exhaust fans for 48 hours.

Day 14 to 15. Parasitic *Monodontomerus* wasps begin emerging. Native leafcutter bees, if present, will also emerge. At this stage development can be delayed if necessary by lowering the temperature to 65°F (~18°C) for up to one week.

Day 15. Pupae are black in color.

Day 17. Male development complete, screened lids should be in place.

Day 18. Male bees begin emerging. Begin feeding bees if necessary. Black lights should be removed from incubator.

Day 20. Female bees begin to emerge.

Day 23. 50 percent of females should have emerged. Bees can be released in the field.

Day 32. All bees should have emerged.

Parasite Control during Incubation

Some producers cover loose cells with a 1-inch (2.54-centimeter) layer of sawdust or vermiculite during incubation. It is thought that bees and parasites can work their way through this material, but that parasitic wasps cannot return through the material to re-infest other cells. Perlite should not be used for this purpose as it contains a static charge that can adhere to the hairs on the bee's body.

Prior to beginning incubation, black lights and water pans should be in place (figure 7.21). These light traps consist of a water-filled tray to which a few drops of detergent are added to break the surface tension. Mounted above the tray is a black light. Parasitic insects, especially chalcid wasps, are attracted to the ultraviolet light and drown in the water. Because some parasitic insects are poor fliers, these light traps should be located on the floor of the incubation room, so that they can hop down to the light traps rather than trying to climb up to them. A single window located in the incubation room can be used instead of a black light, again with a water-filled tray placed below the window. Remember bees will also be attracted to these light traps, and screened covers should be in place on the incubation trays prior to emergence. Screened lids do not necessarily need to be in place until male bees begin to emerge, and in some instances the lids may hinder the removal of parasites from the incubator. The walls of the incubation room should also be vacuumed several times a day to remove chalcid wasps. See Appendix A, page 114, for more information on controlling pest insects during incubation.

Canadian leafcutter producers have a long-standing practice of placing dichlorvos (Vapona™) pest strips inside incubation rooms during the early

Eric Mader

Figure 7.21 A homemade light trap to control chalcid wasps. The trap consists of a black light suspended over a pan of water containing a few drops of detergent to reduce surface tension. Light traps should be maintained in incubators and anywhere dormant leafcutter or mason bees are stored. Note the large numbers of drowned wasps in the pan.

stages of pupal development. These strips are then removed after several days, and the room is aerated to remove any remaining vapors. If timed correctly, the dichlorvos strips are very effective at killing parasitic chalcid wasps. When not timed correctly, not properly vented, or under high humidity conditions, dichlorvos can be extremely lethal to bees. These pest strips are not labeled for this use in the US; using them in leafcutter operations is illegal, potentially dangerous to both bee and the beekeeper alike, and their use is not recommended. Similarly some Canadian producers have recently begun fumigating nest equipment and incubating cells with high concentrations of formaldehyde gas to control chalkbrood disease. The beekeepers that do this require extensive protective equipment and chemicals to neutralize the gas during venting. This is an extremely hazardous process that has not been approved in the US. It should not be attempted.

Prior to my current work as the Xerces Society's Pollinator Outreach Coordinator, I worked as a crop consultant and contract beekeeper, providing pollination services for dozens of crop species across the Midwest (figure 7.22).

But keeping leafcutter bees was something that I never initially intended to do. I knew what they were, and I already had some experience with honey bees and mason bees. But leafcutter bees seemed somehow anachronistic—a reminder of my childhood in North Dakota where abandoned plywood bee shelters dot the Canadian border, collapsing a little more with every prairie winter.

As my pollination work grew, however, I began to see the need for an alternative. Specifically I needed a bee that was active in the summer, that could be deployed on large acres of diverse crops, and that would not abandon the bloom when something better was available down the road. Honey bees met most of those criteria, but not the last one—honey bees often favor distant weeds like sweet clover over marginally

Eric Mader

Figure 7.22 The author, Eric Mader, installing a leafcutter bee shelter.

LEAFCUTTER BEEKEEPING: A NOTE FROM THE AUTHOR

appealing crops like onions growing adjacent to their hives.

Leafcutter bees seemed like the logical solution. But where was the information? The few extension-type publications I could find were decades old. In the end I had to rely on various Canadian publications geared specifically towards alfalfa producers. From what I had read, the process was simple: set up the nest blocks, release the bees, and let nature take its course.

Nature did take its course, and soon I was battling every type of bee parasite and disease imaginable—things that apparently don't exist in Canada! Woodpeckers and chipmunks made quick work of my expensive imported Styrofoam nest blocks. And windstorms sent the bee shelters sailing off into the next county. Even my initial bee stock, ordered from Canada, was doomed from the beginning—held up at the border for several weeks by Customs authorities. I think I made every mistake imaginable when starting out.

And yet I persevered.

Over the years I provided pollination services with leafcutter bees on dozens of crop species—everything from rattlesnake master to sunflower. After a lot of experimentation and adaptation of Canadian practices to my local conditions, I began to see more success than failure.

The ongoing plight of honey bees has taught us that our dependence on a single managed pollinator is a risky proposition, one that has the potential for catastrophic results to our fruit, vegetable, forage, and oil crop industries. Viable alternative wild and managed pollinators are essential, and leafcutters can be part of the solution.

8 Other Managed Pollinators

Eric Mader, *Pollinator Outreach Coordinator, the Xerces Society for Invertebrate Conservation*

Aside from mason bees, bumble bees, and leafcutter bees, there are a number of less commonly managed pollinators—the "alternatives to alternatives," so to speak. For the most part, management systems for these species remain largely underdeveloped, and there is much room for adaptation, experimentation, and improvement.

In many cases practical applications for the insects described in this chapter—alkali bees, shaggy fuzzyfoot bees, and flies—are limited to very specific operations or environments. And while their use may not be practical for most growers or beekeepers, they may serve as a model for the development of new managed pollinators.

The Alkali Bee
(*Nomia melanderi*)

Along with the alfalfa leafcutter bee (see chapter 7, page 75), alfalfa seed production in the US has historically been linked to the alkali bee (*Nomia melanderi*), a ground-nesting bee native to arid regions in the western US. The alkali bee's affinity for alfalfa blossoms (see sidebar: Alfalfa Pollination, page 79) was first recognized by forage producers in the 1940s. Following the development of management techniques in the late 1950s, growers using the alkali bee have produced astounding yields of up to

2,400 pounds of cleaned seed per acre (~2,700 kilograms per hectare)—this in the normally unproductive desert regions of the Great Basin. Interest in the alkali bee declined in the late 1960s and 1970s due to rising interest in alfalfa leafcutter bees. Managed populations also suffered in many areas during this time after several seasons of heavy rainfall, which led to mold spoilage of previously productive nest sites.

Most recently, the alkali bee has been employed for pollination of other crops including sweet clover, mint, onion, and celery. Alkali bees are currently the only managed soil-nesting bee in North America—a surprising fact given that the vast majority of bee species nest below ground.

Because they are ground nesters, alkali bees cannot be easily transported, and their usefulness is confined to arid locations where flooding is rare—typically flat alkaline desert soils. Within these playas or "salt flats," individual bee nests are usually located in the upper 8 inches (~20 centimeters) of soil and consist of tunnel entrances with a series of brood chambers located below the surface (figure 8.1).

To achieve adequate pollination, crops must be located within 5 miles (8 kilometers) of a nest site. Where naturally occurring nest sites are rare, artificial nests can be constructed. This process can be labor intensive and may require the use of finely ground rock salt or table salt (NaCl) as a soil amendment.

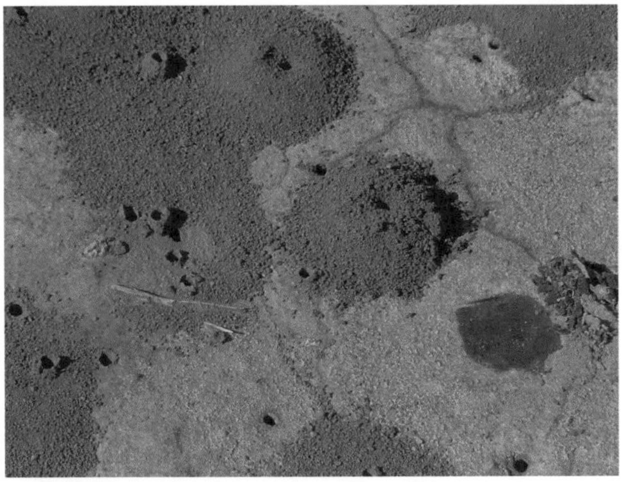

Figure 8.1 Alkali bee nest sites are recognizable by the mounds of excavated soil called tumuli.

Figure 8.2
The alkali bee (*Nomia melanderi*) is the only managed ground-nesting bee in the US.

Life Cycle

Alkali bees are members of the Halictidae family, which includes a diverse array of other solitary ground-nesting species—often called "sweat bees" for their occasional attraction to the salt present in human perspiration. Alkali bees average 7/16 inch (11 millimeters) in length and are generally dark colored with iridescent gold or green bands on the abdomen (figure 8.2). Male bees are distinguished by their longer antennae and lack of stinger.

Like alfalfa leafcutter bees and mason bees, the alkali bee is a solitary species. Individual females construct and provision their own nests, and have no contact with other female bees. However, like other managed solitary bees, the alkali bee is gregarious and nests in close proximity to others of its own kind.

Nests are constructed in the crusted-over soils of wet alkali flats. In these areas, capillary action from high water tables brings salt and minerals to the surface where crystals are deposited as the water evaporates. These minerals form a thin crust limiting further evaporation and maintaining a moist nesting environment in the otherwise arid region of the bee's native range. Under optimal conditions 1 cubic foot (28.3 liters) of alkaline soil may contain up to 50 nest cells.

Individual nests consist of a single vertical tunnel slightly less than ½ inch (12.7 millimeters) in diameter, from 3 inches to 16 inches deep (7.6 to 41 centimeters). Short oval-shaped cavities branch off from the main entrance tunnel, resulting in a series of individual cells about ½ inch in length (figure 8.3). Within an individual nest there may be up to 15 or 20 of these smaller cells. These cells are provisioned with a sticky mixture of pollen and nectar formed into balls by the nesting female. Typically eight to ten separate foraging trips are required to collect the necessary pollen.

An egg is laid on top of the pollen ball (figure 8.4, page 96) and it hatches within three days. As with

Figure 8.3 Soil profile of *Nomia melandera* nest. Brood cells provisioned with a ball of pollen and egg are visible at the ends of the soil tunnels.

Figure 8.4 Close-up of brood cell with *N. melandera* egg laid on a pollen ball.

other bees, female alkali bees control the sex of their offspring by laying a fertilized egg, which develops into a female bee—or by laying an unfertilized egg, which develops into a male.

Over the next eight days the young larva grows until reaching its full size and then remains dormant as a full sized larva for up to ten months—typically over the winter. The following summer the larva undergoes pupation, changing into a recognizable tunnel, with the soil that is removed being deposited around the entrance hole in a conical mound 2 to 3 inches across (5.1 to 7.6 centimeters) (resembling an ant hill, but with a larger entrance). As the tunnel and individual cells are excavated, the nesting female applies a transparent secretion from her tongue to the tunnel walls. This secretion forms a waterproof cement, which maintains the structural integrity of the walls and prevents flooding. Individual cells are also sealed off with a soil plug made from tunnel soil excavations during the nesting process. About one cell is completed each day.

Mating occurs immediately upon female emergence, which is normally preceded a day or two earlier by male emergence. Males patrol over the nesting area and pounce on females as they emerge from the ground. A single male may mate with multiple females. After mating, the female bee will live for approximately one month. During that time she will normally construct a single nest tunnel containing up to 20 cells.

Artificial Nest Sites

Because of its selective nesting requirements, the alkali bee is susceptible to habitat loss and now is uncommon in parts of its original range. In fact the early success of the alkali bee has contributed to its decline in some areas as growers expanded field sizes to take advantage of abundant local bee populations, often plowing up productive nest areas in the process. In other areas, off-road vehicle traffic and cattle grazing have resulted in extensive habitat loss. However, artificially constructed soil beds continue to provide some habitat in the alfalfa seed production regions of the Great Basin and Pacific Northwest.

These artificial beds typically consist of an excavated trench, usually two to three feet deep, which is then lined with a pond liner, thick plastic sheeting or an impermeable layer of bentonite clay. If a plastic liner is used, it should be covered with a layer of straw or soil to protect against punctures. Next a 5-inch (12.7-centimeter) layer of gravel is added to the bed. Above this initial gravel layer, vertical standpipes are installed roughly 50 feet (~15 meters) apart with perforated drain pipes radiating outward throughout the gravel layer. Above these drain pipes an additional 5 inches (12.7 centimeters) of gravel is added, and covered with straw, burlap, or landscape fabric to prevent soil infiltration of the gravel layer. Finally the soil is backfilled over the bed and lightly compacted. When finished the bed should be slightly elevated so that rain water does not pool on top of the nest site.

Artificial beds of this type should ideally be constructed in silty loam soils with no more than seven percent clay. As water is added to the standpipes, moisture will rise to the surface and should create a firm layer of salt, which seals in soil moisture and slows further evaporation of water from the bed. If the soil is not adequately saline, salt can be mixed with water and added to the standpipes. More commonly, salt is often applied to the surface at a rate of 1 pound per square foot (~5 kilograms per square meter) and raked into the upper 2 inches (5 centimeters) of soil.

The final result is a standing water reservoir below ground with a constant supply of moisture extending upward to a crusted-over surface which reduces evaporation. Maintaining this soil moisture consistently between 8 and 35 percent in the upper layer of the bed where bees are actively nesting is critical. Soil tensiometers provide a quick and easy moisture measurement, and, as necessary, water can be added to the standpipes. If excessive soil drying becomes a problem during the nesting season, bee beds can be shaded with either nursery shade cloth or military surplus camouflage netting suspended above the bed on permanent posts.

Alkali bees may find the artificial bed if other natural or managed nest sites are located within a mile or so. Often however, the bed may have to be stocked with bees, either as adults, or as larvae, acquired from other growers. Dormant larvae are typically installed into the bed as 1 cubic foot (0.028 cubic meters) blocks of undisturbed soil from established beds. This is normally performed during the winter when the larvae are inactive. Such soil blocks may contain more than 50 larvae.

Adult bees may also be released at the new nest site; however, results may not be as successful, especially if the bees were collected within 10 miles (16 kilometers) of the new bed. Adult bees are typically stocked by collecting them with insect nets at established beds and releasing them at the new bed after dark. Small holes are often punched into the bed with a pitchfork to encourage the released bees to remain at the new site.

There is little published information regarding optimal bed size for managed alkali bee populations. The general consensus among alfalfa growers seems to be the larger the better. Beds of around an acre (0.40 hectare) in size may produce thousands, or even millions of bees. In fact in some areas, growers' cooperatives manage these sorts of community beds, and since alkali bees may forage up to 5 miles (8 kilometers) or more, they provide pollination services for multiple farms. The drawback with such large beds is that bees traveling greater distances have the potential for increased pesticide exposure in densely culti-vated regions. Where conditions can support these sorts of bee beds, the initial installation and ongoing maintenance costs are a bargain compared to annual honey bee rental or purchased leafcutter bees.

Individually, a female alkali bee begins foraging an hour or two after sunrise and continues until an hour or two before sunset. She may average a pollination rate of 12 alfalfa flowers per minute, or around 2,000 flowers per day. In the one month of her active adult life, a female alkali bee may pollinate up to 25,000 flowers, resulting in up to a third of a pound of alfalfa seed. As with most other bee species, male alkali bees visit flowers for nectar only and are not considered effective pollinators.

Additional Management Practices

In natural settings, the alkali bee forages on common scrubland plants like Russian thistle, greasewood, cleome, locoweed, and morning glory. Even among managed populations, these wild plants are important supplemental food sources and should be allowed to grow as an alternate food source when the main crop is not in bloom. Bee populations without adequate forage sources throughout their nesting period are likely to decline after several seasons.

In addition to alternate forage sources, both natural and artificial bee beds should be fenced off to prevent vehicle traffic and livestock trampling where necessary. Beds should be kept free of weeds to maintain an attractive bare surface. Beds should not be flooded during the active nesting season if possible.

Pesticide use should be reduced or eliminated during the nesting period, and blooming plants should not be sprayed at all while alkali bees are active. For more information on reducing bee losses to pesticides, see Appendix D, page 130.

As with other solitary managed bees, the female alkali bee has a stinger but rarely uses it. Protective clothing, such as bee suits and veils used for honey beekeeping, is unnecessary when working around alkali bees.

Parasites and Diseases

Alkali bees are attacked by a number of parasites and diseases; however as with other management aspects for this species, little research has been performed. Among the most notable pests are the bomber flies (*Heterostylum robustum*), and the black blister beetle (*Meloe nigra*). The larvae of both species feed on the developing alkali bee larvae. The bomber flies are notable for depositing their eggs into bee nests while hovering above tunnel entrances (see figure 8.5, below). The egg soon hatches and the fly maggot burrows into a cell containing the developing bee, which it devours. Female blister beetles on the other hand crawl directly into nest entrances and lay their eggs in a suitable cell. Developing beetle larvae consume both the pollen-nectar provision and the developing bee.

Other reported pests of alkali bee larvae include the flesh fly (*Euphytomina nomivora*), the thick-headed fly (*Zondion obliquefasciatum*), various ambush bugs, tiger beetles, checkered flower beetles, chalcid wasps, ants, spiders, mites, and cuckoo bees, which kill the alkali bee larvae, and consume

their food provisions. Larger animals such as birds, rodents, and skunks may also prey upon both immature and adult alkali bees.

In addition, various bacterial, fungal, and possibly viral pathogens may attack developing larvae. Food provisions are also prone to spoilage by yeasts and molds under wet conditions. As with animal pests, few established control measures exist for diseases.

The Shaggy Fuzzyfoot Bee
(*Anthophora pilipes villosula*)

Among the least common managed bees in the US is the shaggy fuzzyfoot. This solitary bee is native to Europe and Asia, and is a relatively recent introduction in the US—imported from Japan in the early 1990s by the USDA Bee Research Lab in Beltsville, Maryland.

The fuzzyfoot is a fairly large bee that superficially resembles a drab bumble bee. Like bumble bees, the fuzzyfoot is reputed to have some thermoregulatory ability, and is capable of generating body heat—allowing the bee to forage even in cool and wet conditions. However, this bee apparently has limited winter hardiness, and its management is restricted to warm, humid climates.

Nesting for the fuzzyfoot occurs in exposed vertical banks or dry adobe. Female bees construct cavities by first softening dry mud with nectar or saliva, then they produce an oily secretion which is used to line the brood cells. Stackable adobe blocks, sheltered against rain and moisture, are used as a managed nesting system. Like some other cavity nesting bees, the fuzzyfoot is gregarious and tends to locate nests near its own natal home.

Fuzzyfoot bees are reportedly excellent pollinators of high-bush blueberries, both in the southern US and in Japan. Adult foraging lasts roughly three weeks during the spring, and there is one generation each year.

The Blue Bottle Fly
(*Calliphora vomitoria*)

With the unsettling scientific name of *Calliphora vomitoria*, the common blue bottle fly is perhaps our most unusual managed pollinator (figure 8.6). Even to describe the blue bottle fly as a "managed polli-

Edward S. Ross

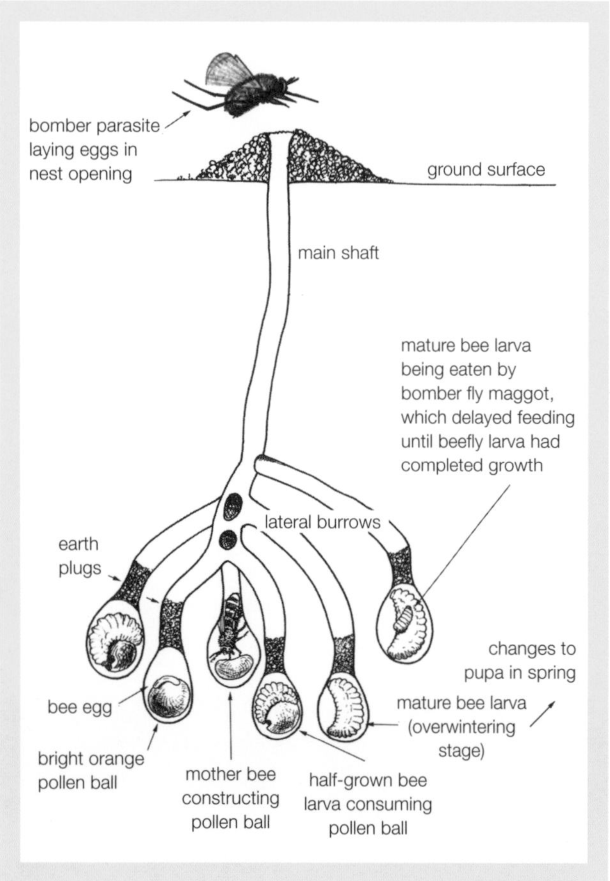

Figure 8.5 Cross section of a typical alkali bee nest showing the work of one parent female. The cells show various stages in the life history of her offspring and the bomber fly parasite.

Figure 8.6 Blue bottle flies on carrot flowers.

nator" is to stretch the definition of the term since the fly is only an incidental pollinator, and its management practices are minimal. Yet for certain plant breeding operations, the blue bottle fly is an effective and important alternative to bee pollination.

As a member of the Calliphoridae, or blow fly family, the blue bottle fly is often considered a nuisance. Its associated foods—rotting flesh and dung—give the insect a reputation for spreading disease. However, these dietary habits also serve to keep the world clean and to recycle nutrients. The larval maggot stage of flies uses the protein in these foods for development. Female adult flies also consume a small amount of these foods as a protein source for the development of mature eggs within their ovaries. The primary fuel source for flight activity in adult flies, however, is sugar—such as that found in flower nectar. It is this dietary requirement that can be harnessed for managed plant pollination.

Currently the use of managed blue bottle flies has been limited primarily to vegetable breeding programs, particularly members of the carrot family, including carrot, parsnip, dill, and celery.

At about ½ inch in length (12.7 millimeters), the blue bottle fly is slightly larger than the common house fly (*Musca domestica*). Blue bottle flies have conspicuous red eyes and short blunt antennae. The head and thorax are a nondescript gray color, and the abdomen is metallic blue. While they do have patches of short hair covering their body, flies do not have any special pollen collecting structures, nor do they actively gather pollen. While some pollen grains

inadvertently stick to them while feeding on nectar, blue bottle flies are not optimized for large-scale movement of pollen.

Also unlike bees, flies do not construct or provision nests for their offspring. As a result flies have no special homing instinct and will not return to specific flowers or locations. Their use as managed pollinators is therefore restricted to cages, screened rooms, or sealed greenhouses that prevent escape (figure 8.7). Typically these pollination scenarios involve specialized breeding programs utilizing small batches of isolated plants. In these sorts of confinement situations, bees may become sullen and refuse to forage, or need supplemental food sources. In close quarters confinement, flies may also be preferable to bees due to stinging concerns. In addition, depending on the time of year, certain bee species may not be available or may require artificial incubation and lifecycle manipulation for adult emergence. Flies on the other hand are readily available from professional rearing facilities year-round. These insectary-reared flies are very low cost, and are typically reared in sanitary conditions to prevent the spread of infectious disease. Purchased flies are usually shipped as pupae ready for emergence, sometimes in heated shipping boxes, which act as incubators (see sidebar, page 100).

Rearing procedures for blue bottle flies are well established. Captive adult populations are maintained in screened cages. These adults can either be procured from established producers or wild collected. Rearing

Figure 8.7 Blue bottle flies confined to a large field pollination cage at a USDA-ARS vegetable breeding research station.

room conditions are typically maintained at around 78°F (~25°C) and 30 to 40 percent relative humidity. A daily cycle of 14 hours of light and 10 hours of darkness seems to be preferable.

Adult flies are provided water at all times through cotton dental rolls that wick water from an enclosed reservoir. A provision of honey is also maintained at all times, and is changed twice weekly as needed to prevent spoilage.

In addition to the water and honey, adult flies require a supplemental food source to promote egg laying. A recipe used by the USDA-ARS North Cen-

---

FLY POLLINATION: A PLANT BREEDER'S PERSPECTIVE

When Rob Kane (figure 8.8) began breeding carrots for the USDA-Agriculture Research Service in Madison, Wisconsin, honey bees were the pollinator of choice. But there were problems.

To prevent pollen contamination by wild carrots or carrots of the wrong variety, the plants are grown in screened cages. "The bees always seemed depressed or hungry in the cages," Rob says. "They spent a lot of time fanning themselves to keep cool during hot weather, and they didn't really work the flowers." To further complicate matters, Rob's field assistants were afraid of getting stung by the honey bees, so maintenance tasks inside the cages—like weeding—were often ignored.

And the bees were expensive. A single honey bee nuc (a miniature bee hive), rented from a local beekeeper cost $80. With dozens of large screened cages in need of individual nucs, the costs quickly added up.

Rob's department had a small basement facility for rearing houseflies (*Musca domestica*), which were used for pollination in the greenhouse during winter months. The small houseflies, while adequate, were also less than ideal—especially for the big outdoor cages during the summer when a lot of pollen needs to be moved between plants quickly.

When Rob tried blue bottle flies from an outside vendor, he was impressed. "You see all those flies working that flower," Rob says pointing to a single carrot flower covered with nearly a dozen flies. "That's what a seed-man wants to see." The larger blue bottle flies have numerous advantages: they have a natural affinity for umbelliferous flowers like carrot; they don't sting; they are available on demand through overnight shipping from the supplier; and they are inexpensive. "I think we figured the cost out once to be about four flies to the penny," he says.

Just like other pollinators, blue bottle flies have their limitations. "You have to watch them during really hot weather, and give them a little water. Their lifespan in the field is about 10 days; then you have to restock them. We usually just add about a handful a week to the large 12 feet x 12 feet or 12 feet x 24 feet cages during flowering." (3.7 meters x 3.7 meters or 3.7 meters x 7.3 meters) Aside from that, the flies are maintenance free, allowing Rob to focus on his real task—producing better carrots.

Contact Rob Kane
Agricultural Science Research Technician
USDA-ARS
Vegetable Crops Research Unit
(608) 262-2168
rtkane@wisc.edu

Rob's fly vendor:
Forked Tree Ranch
HCR 60, Box 226
Porthill, ID 83853
(208) 267-2632
www.forkedtreeranch.com

Rob Kane

Figure 8.8 Rob Kane observing flies pollinating a carrot plant in his vegetable breeding greenhouse.

tral Region Plant Introduction Station (NCRPIS) in Ames, Iowa consists of 35 milliliters corn syrup mixed with 10 grams of dry powdered egg, and 1 teaspoon alphacel (a food grade cellulose product). These ingredients are mixed to form a sticky paste that is provided to the flies in a petri dish and covered with a plastic mesh screen as a feeding platform. Fresh food is provided weekly as necessary.

Adult females lay their eggs on a larval food source, typically beef organs such as small pieces of raw liver, roughly 3 inches x 3 inches (7.6 x 7.6 centimeters). To provide additional egg laying surface area, the liver may be scored deeply with a knife. It is then placed into a Petri dish and placed into the cage containing adult flies. The NCRPIS recommends placing this Petri dish in a shaded or covered area within the rearing cage to further encourage egg laying. The eggs are slightly over one millimeter in length, and a female fly may lay up to 200 at one time. Hatching time requires about one day under warm indoor temperatures.

After 24 hours the piece of liver is removed from the rearing cage and transferred to a second Petri dish containing a larval food source that is less prone to spoilage. The NCRPIS uses a diet containing 180 grams of blood meal, 120 grams dried egg, 120 grams dried milk, 6 grams sorbic acid, and 6 grams methyl paraben. The last two ingredients act as preservatives. These dry ingredients are premixed, and will produce about three liters of finished larval food.

To prepare the larval food, 54 grams of agar is mixed with 1.8 liters of distilled water and cooked in a microwave until the solution turns gold in color and is bubbling from the bottom. This is then poured slowly into a large laboratory blender containing 2.25 liters of distilled water (which serves as a cooling agent). This mixture is blended together and the dry ingredients are then added. After further blending, 3 milliliters of propionic/phosphoric acid solution is added. This acid solution acts as a fungicide in the final product, reducing spoilage during larval feeding. Extreme care should be taken when handling this, and all other ingredients, and appropriate protective equipment such as gloves, goggles, and aprons should be worn.

After several minutes of mixing, this is poured into Petri dishes, covered with clean paper towels, and allowed to dry. Drying may take up to one hour.

After the diet is solid, and no moisture remains, it can be covered with a plastic bag and stored in the refrigerator. To allow the acid solution to combine with the other ingredients, it should not be fed to the larvae until 24 hours have passed following preparation. It should also be warmed to room temperature before it is transferred to the rearing cage.

Before preparation it is essential that all cookware, countertops, and utensils are sterilized with a weak bleach solution.

After about 24 hours the first larvae appear. These larvae then develop through three growth stages, called instars. Each instar is separated by a molting event. At this stage the maggots are white with black mouth hooks that are used to tear flesh while feeding. Enzymes are also secreted to help break down food sources during the feeding process.

Upon hatching the small first instars begin crawling in search of additional food. During this stage the raw liver is placed directly on top of the manufactured larval food source in a smaller dish—after the larvae move to the manufactured food, the original liver can be removed. Additional manufactured food is supplied as needed. Moldy food should be discarded.

Feeding maggots are maintained in tightly screened containers. In the search for food and pupation areas, maggots may climb throughout the container where they will discover any potential escape holes.

After a week or more of feeding, the larvae begin pupation. In nature, fly maggots burrow into the soil and remain covered with tough brown cocoons while they develop into adults. These pupae may remain dormant over winter during cool weather; however, in warm conditions, they will emerge as mature adult flies in two to three weeks.

In the rearing facility, after a week of active feeding on the manufactured larval food, vermiculite is added to the floor of the rearing cage forming a layer about 1 inch (2.54 centimeters) deep. Pupation will then begin as the maggots burrow into vermiculite. After an additional five days this vermiculite is then chilled for 24 hours in a 40°F (4.4°C) refrigerator. Pupae are then separated from the vermiculite using a series of screened trays.

Upon separation from the vermiculite, pupae can be added directly to pollination cages for emergence within several days (figure 8.9, page 102). An indi-

Figure 8.9 Small pollination cages prevent flies from dispersing and prevent contamination by outside pollen sources.

vidual female fly may lay up to 2,000 eggs over her lifetime, which is typically about one month. The sex ratio of these eggs is usually 50:50. The rate of development and emergence is very much temperature dependent with temperatures from 75° to 80°F (24° to 27°C) producing rapid maturation.

If bloom times are delayed, or if adult flies are not needed immediately, pupae can be stored for several weeks at 40°F (4.4°C) to delay emergence. For each day of cold storage, emergence may be delayed by several days.

Blue bottle flies are widespread throughout North America; however, these rearing procedures may require modification depending on local conditions. In particular, low-humidity climates may increase pupal mortality under storage conditions. In these situations, additional humidity sources may be required to prevent desiccation of dormant cocoons.

9 The Search for New Managed Pollinators

Eric Mader, *Pollinator Outreach Coordinator, the Xerces Society for Invertebrate Conservation*

Despite the variety of choices currently available, the search for new managed pollinators goes on. Specialty crops often require specialty pollinators, and local conditions often require locally sourced pollinator species. While wild pollinator conservation is a key component to sustainability, managed pollinators will remain necessary wherever large-scale monoculture cropping occurs.

The selection and isolation of these new pollinators from currently wild species should be pursued with caution and controlled enthusiasm. Paramount in the process should be the ongoing well being of wild populations. When they are managed in unnaturally large numbers, parasites and diseases are inevitable. Care should be taken to limit their spread. Similarly, the introduction of new managed pollinators should be conducted with careful deliberation and in a process that involves both agricultural and ecological expertise.

In a search for new manageable pollinator species, bees will inevitably remain the most profitable, especially the cavity-nesting species, for which there are already several model systems. Development of techniques for management of ground-nesting bees—which constitute the vast majority of all species—remains an area ripe for exploration (figure 9.1).

Eric Mader

Figure 9.1
Ground-nesting native bees, like this *Agopostemon* species, can play a significant role in crop pollination, but only if sufficient habitat is available to support them.

Cavity-Nesting Bees

While the alfalfa leafcutter and blue orchard bees have been the focus of much attention, numerous other cavity-nesting bees have management potential. Most of these bees lack common names and are not well studied, but their nesting requirements are largely understood.

A simple way to isolate these wild bees and select new species for future management is through the use of observation nests. Such nests typically consist of a grooved nest board (with a series of dead-end tunnels routered along one side), which is then covered with a tight-fitting transparent cover (figure

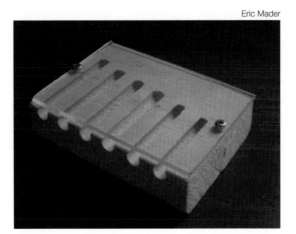

Eric Mader

Figure 9.2 An observation nest for cavity-nesting bees consists of a series of routered channels and a transparent cover. Different hole diameters and depths appeal to different bee species. The transparent cover should be covered with an opaque material to encourage nesting.

9.2). Since light infiltration discourages cavity-nesting bees, the transparent cover should be shielded by some sort of opaque material that can be easily removed.

Ideally these types of observation hives should have a variety of hole sizes and depths, and they should be placed in areas where cavity-nesting bees are likely to be found: near old wooden barns, fallen trees, or brush piles, for example. The nests can be monitored for activity by periodically removing the opaque covering and examining the nest interior though the transparent cover. The type of food pro-

vision and cell partition present can then be used to identify most bees down to the family and genus level—even during immature stages (table 9.1). Note that when the food provision consists of other insects such as grasshoppers or spiders it means the cavity is not occupied by an immature bee, but rather by a predatory wasp.

After checking the contents of the observation nest, it should be placed back in its original position. Painting the fronts of the nests different colors will help reduce disorientation by returning foragers.

The majority of cavity-nesting bees belong to the Megachilidae family. Among these are many species that seal off their cell partitions with strong, glue-like plant resins. While these bees are interesting to observe, they present unique management challenges, and would probably require some sort of disposable nesting system (such as a drilled block with paper inserts) for active management.

Ground-Nesting Bees

Perhaps the most underdeveloped aspect of bee culture is the management and conservation of our short-tongued bees—most of which are solitary subterranean nesters. Vast numbers of Halictid, Andrenid, and Colletid bees range the Earth—leading hidden lives played out in small dark tunnels excavated in cliff faces, barren desert ground, or beneath rock surfaces. Few people have attempted

Table 9.1
Identifying Cavity-Nesting Bees by Nest Construction

CELL PARTITION MATERIAL	ADULT COLOR OR PATTERN	FAMILY	GENERA	COMMON NAME
Mud, chewed plant material	Metallic, solid black, occasionally other	Megachilidae	*Osmia, Hoplitis*	Mason bees
Plant resins, sand, pebbles	Striped	Megachilidae	*Chelostomoides*	Resin bees
Cut or chewed leaf sections	Striped	Megachilidae	*Megachile*	Leafcutter bees
Compacted fibers, or hair, resins, sand	Black and yellow or black and white	Megachilidae	*Anthidium*	Carder bees
Compacted sawdust	Various colors	Apidae	*Xylocopa, Centris*	Carpenter bees
Plastic-like membrane	Various colors	Colletidae	*Hylaeus*	Masked bees

Note: When the food provision consists of other insects, the cavity is occupied by a predatory wasp, not a bee.

to quantify the global populations of these bees or the value they have as pollinators of wild and cultivated plants. But without a doubt our dependence on them is enormous.

Despite our indifference, and even occasional hostility, these animals constitute the vast majority of the bee species—around 70 percent in fact. The lifecycle of these bees often mirrors that of solitary, aboveground cavity-nesting bees. Typically a single female constructs and provisions a nest, lays an egg, and seals off the chamber where her offspring will develop alone. Unlike her aboveground counterparts, the ground-nesting bee must excavate an elaborate nest chamber with a single tunnel opening to the surface (figure 9.3) and a series of lateral tunnels leading to a dozen or more individual brood chambers. In some cases these tunnels may extend several feet below ground, and may be lined with glandular glue-like secretions that prevent the walls from collapsing when flooded. Often the only aboveground sign of all this work is a pile of excavated soil, or tumulus (resembling an ant mound).

The countless environmental factors that make a particular site appealing to a particular species are unknown, but where they are found, productive spots may contain multiple nests per square foot—comprising aggregations of thousands of nesting females. The great model for ground-nesting bee-keeping is the alkali bee (see page 94). While many of the management practices associated with the alkali bee are species specific, some of those principles may transfer to the management of other bees.

The most basic (and obvious) requirement is the need for a bare soil surface that is protected from regular tillage and motor vehicle traffic (including ATVs). Loose, friable, and sandy soils that are easy to excavate are especially preferred by many ground-nesting bees. The required amount of soil moisture varies between species, with some bees preferring dry, fast-draining soils, while others tolerate seasonal flooding. Many species prefer south-facing, or otherwise sun-exposed areas.

Several types of artificial nest sites can be created with minimal effort. The first is simply to create and maintain bare patches of ground adjacent to productive floral sources. A slightly more involved, but possibly more productive nest site can be created with

Eric Mader

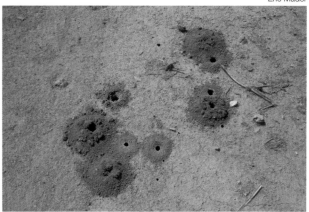

Figure 9.3 These holes in the ground betray the presence of ground-nesting bees. The farmer cultivated this field shortly after the photo was taken. The same farmer rents honey bees for pollination each year.

small mounds of packed sand or agricultural lime. A more elaborate nest site that resembles a cliff face can be created by constructing a stone wall, with soil packed between the individual stones.

A very productive nest site for ground-nesting bees, but one that is difficult to create artificially, is the soil-covered root mass of wind-fallen trees. Such natural sites may be of value for the acquisition of bee larvae to "seed" new, artificial nests (as is done with the alkali bee).

Beyond Beekeeping

While most of this book has focused on bees, good rearing information exists for many other insect species. For example, vast numbers of fly species—currently assaulted with aerosol cans, bug zappers, and fly swatters—may, in the future, be harnessed as dual-purpose pollinators and biocontrol agents, preying upon crop pests like aphids, and doing our pollinating in the process.

The European honey bee is overworked and undervalued. With every publicized crisis she is telling us that she needs a rest. Alternative managed pollinators are not a substitute for the honey bee, but they are a supplement on the road to a holistic multi-species approach to crop pollination. It's impossible to know exactly how we will reach that destination, but the insects discussed in this book, along with innumerable anonymous insect heroes, will be part of the process.

10 Habitat Conservation for Native Pollinators

Eric Mader, *Pollinator Outreach Coordinator, the Xerces Society for Invertebrate Conservation*

North America has around 4,000 native bee species. And while bees are arguably the most important group of animal pollinators, they are not the only ones. Countless wasps, butterflies, moths, flies, beetles, hummingbirds, and even bats contribute to the pollination of various plants. Around the world, even more unusual examples of animal pollinators exist, including mosquitoes, slugs, rainforest lizards, an Australian possum, and even lemurs on the island of Madagascar.

In addition to pollinating flowers, these creatures play a critical role in the larger ecosystem. Wasps and syrphid fly larvae for example prey upon plant pests like aphids and locusts (figure 10.2). Pollinator insects like bees are food for larger animals such as birds and amphibians. The seeds and fruit pollinated by insects feed countless larger animals like rodents

and bears. And some plants are dependent on specific pollinators for reproduction—such as bottle gentian (*Gentiana andrewsii*) by bumble bees and cardinal flower (*Lobelia cardinalis*) by hummingbirds.

Protecting these wild pollinators is expensive, but not protecting them costs much more. Many of our own food, fiber, and medicinal plants are entirely dependent on insects for pollination.

Against the backdrop of our rising dependence on insect pollination is a critical decline in the numbers and diversity of wild pollinators. Habitat loss and fragmentation has pushed our native pollinators to the margins of human civilization. Vast areas of wild lupine, once common in the Great Lakes region, have been lost to urbanization. The Karner Blue butterfly (figure 10.3) has nearly been lost because it depends on lupine during its caterpillar stage. Various other

Figure 10.1

Osmia aglaia is just one of several wild bee species being studied for their potential as managed pollinators, in this case for raspberry production.

Figure 10.2

A dual-purpose beneficial insect: this syrphid fly (*Syrphus ribesii*) is an overlooked pollinator whose larvae prey upon pest insects like aphids.

Figure 10.3
Once common in the Great Lakes region, the Karner Blue butterfly (*Lycaeides Melissa-samuelis*), is now endangered. As wild lupine, the caterpillar's food source, has disappeared, so has the butterfly.

Figure 10.4
Bees killed by pesticide poisoning in an agricultural field.

butterflies, once common to North America, are already extinct.

Similarly natural habitats that remain are often degraded. Invasive plant species displace entire ecosystems. Invasive insects attack or displace native ones. And exotic diseases can cause total extinction. In the 1990s European insectaries began rearing American bumble bees for shipment to greenhouse growers in California. Some of these captive bees escaped the California greenhouses. Along with them, it appears that a European strain of *Nosema bombi*, a microsporidian disease endemic to European bumble bees, also escaped. Franklin's bumble bee, once native to the mountains of southern Oregon and northern California, is now believed to be extinct after wild colonies came into contact with the disease. Other once-common bumble bee species including the western (*Bombus occidentalis*), rusty patch (*Bombus affinis*), and yellow-banded bumble bees (*Bombus terricola*) are mysteriously disappearing from large areas of their historic ranges.

In addition to habitat loss and exotic diseases, a century of pesticide use has also taken its toll. Agricultural chemicals are currently labeled for risk to honey bees—a nonnative species. Native bees however receive no similar protection, and because most of our wild pollinators lead solitary lives, their cumulative individual losses to pesticide use go unnoticed (figure 10.4).

While pollinator numbers are in serious decline, the acreage of crops requiring pollination is at an all-time high. The result is that there no longer are enough managed pollinators to go around. Nowhere is this more clear than in the California almond groves. California has more than 1,000 species of native bees, and yet because native bee populations are not large enough to pollinate their trees, almond producers now import honey bees from as far away as Florida and Australia to pollinate the early spring flowers.

The threat of new problems has resulted in tougher standards for the movement of honey bees across state and national borders. Managed hives are increasingly expensive, and some growers now have difficulty obtaining them at any price. Since 1950, the number of managed honey bee hives in the US has declined by 50 percent. As fuel costs continue to rise, pollination beekeepers "following the bloom" from state to state may some day cease.

It's a sad irony that as the world's pollinators decline, our knowledge of them and their incredible value continues to grow. A recent study in California for example concluded that wild bees increase the pollination efficiency of honey bees by up to five times. In the multi-year study of hybrid sunflower production, researchers found that the presence of wild bees causes honey bees to alter their foraging habitats. By interacting with wild bees, honey bees become more skittish causing them to move frequently and visit more flowers.

In many instances wild bees are even better pollinators than the honey bee. There is, for instance, a clear correlation between cranberry yield and native bee abundance. Cranberry flowers release their pollen through small pores on the anthers. A bee can only release this pollen by shaking the anther, similar to shaking salt from a saltshaker. The ability of bumble bees to "buzz pollinate" a flower by vibrating their flight muscles results in more pollen transfer than by honey bees, which are incapable of buzz pollination.

In a study of Massachusetts cranberry fields almost 80 native bee species were found to be associated with cranberry pollination; however, little has been done to encourage these bees or increase their numbers. As the cost of managed honey bees and bumble bees continues to rise, economic and ecological reality can no longer be avoided. If human agriculture is to continue, pollinator conservation must be a priority.

Pollinator Conservation in Farm Settings

Protecting pollinators in agricultural settings begins with whole-farm planning. The layout of fields, woodlots, and waterways all influence the density and diversity of beneficial pollinating insects. Most wild bees for instance only forage a short distance from their nest—often less than 200 yards (~180 meters). If the distances between nest habitat and the crops that need pollination are farther than this, optimal seed set won't be realized. An ideal farm setting for pollinator conservation consists of small fields, 10 acres (~4 hectares) or less, separated by fencerows or buffer strips of naturalized habitat (figure 10.5). Alley cropping, a practice in which row crops are planted between parallel rows of trees, can

be an effective way to create smaller fields while also providing habitat for beneficial insects.

Fallow land may qualify for various USDA conservation programs such as the Conservation Reserve Program (CRP), the Environmental Quality Incentives Program (EQIP), or the Wildlife Habitat Incentives Program (WHIP). Under such programs, landowners who create areas of pollinator-friendly plants may qualify for financial incentives. CRP projects for example can be an excellent opportunity for farmers to make a small amount of money on otherwise marginal land, and provide habitat for pollinators at the same time. For examples of plants that are attractive to wild pollinators and that can be used in these programs, see Table 10.1. Information and application materials for these programs are available from your local USDA Natural Resources Conservation Services (NRCS) office.

Along with land planning, actual production practices have a tremendous impact on pollinator numbers. Two-thirds of all native bee species nest underground. Because of this, ground disturbance should be minimized wherever possible. Extensive tillage in

Eric Mader

Figure 10.5 Restored prairie areas adjacent to agricultural land provide habitat for pollinators and beneficial insects.

Table 10.1
Some Native Perennials for Attracting Wild Pollinators

COMMON NAME	LATIN	BLOOM TIME	NOTES
Willow	*Salix* spp.	Early spring	Extremely important early pollen source for emerging bees
Chokecherry	*Prunus virginiana*	Early spring	Important early pollen source for emerging bees
Maple	*Acer* spp.	Early spring	Early pollen source
Hawthorn	*Crataegus* spp.	Early spring	Early pollen source
Basswood	*Tilia americana*	Spring	Flowers attract many insect species
Wild lupine	*Lupinus* spp.	Spring	Important food source for Karner Blue butterfly, and many bumble bees
Raspberry	*Rubus* spp.	Early summer	Provides pollen and nectar
Fireweed	*Epilobium angustifolium*	Early summer	Abundant nectar source
Sumac	*Rhus sp.*	Early summer	Hollow twigs provide nesting sites for cavity-nesting bees, flowers also valuable
Penstemon	*Penstemon* spp.	Early summer	Various species are attractive to many bees, butterflies, moths, and hummingbirds
Great angelica	*Angelica atropurpurea*	Early summer	Attractive to syrphid flies, and short-tongued bees
Golden alexanders	*Zizia aurea*	Early summer	Attractive to syrphid flies, and short-tongued bees
Figwort	*Scrophularia* spp.	Summer	Abundant nectar source
Wild bergamot	*Monarda* spp.	Summer	All species attract bees, especially bumble bees, as well as hawkmoths, and hummingbirds
Joe-pye weed	*Eupatorium fistulosum*	Summer	Attractive to butterflies
Wild senna	*Cassia hebecarpa*	Summer	Flowers visited by bumble bees; leafcutter bees use leaves for nesting
Hyssop	*Agastache* spp.	Summer	Excellent pollen and nectar plant
Cleome	*Cleome* spp.	Summer	Also called the Rocky Mountain Bee Plant
Milkweed	*Asclepias incarnata*	Summer	Important food source for Monarch butterfly caterpillars
Cardinal flower	*Lobelia cardinalis*	Summer	A hummingbird flower
Blazing-star	*Liatris* spp.	Summer	Very attractive to butterflies
Coneflower	*Echinacea* spp.	Late summer	Very attractive to butterflies and bees
Sunflower	*Helianthus* spp.	Late summer	Wild species better than cultivated varieties
Rattlesnake master	*Eryngium yuccifolium*	Late summer	Abundant pollen and nectar source very attractive to many pollinators
Goldenrod	*Solidago* spp.	Fall	Very important late-season pollen and nectar source
Asters	*Aster* spp.	Late fall	Very late blooming—important for bees preparing for dormancy
Prairie dropseed grass	*Sporobolus heterolepis*	N/A	Provides cover for bumble bee nests
Little bluestem grass	*Andropogon scoparium*	N/A	Provides cover for bumble bee nests

particular can be extremely destructive. Soil fumigation and the use of plastic mulch should also be avoided if possible. Flat areas of well-drained sandy loam should be protected; nest holes suggest the presence of ground-nesting bees. Well-drained sloping soils and north-facing slopes should be protected because they are believed to be used by overwintering bumble bee queens.

Cropping systems may also be optimized to provide food for wild pollinators. Asynchronous planting and planting crops side-by-side that have successive bloom periods will provide floral sources over a longer period of time. Cover crops can also be allowed to flower before they are mowed or plowed under. And bolted crops, like lettuce or radish, might be left in the field until they complete flowering.

Pesticide use can obviously be extremely detrimental to pollinators. In general, the most common pesticides involved in poisoning wild pollinators are the organophosphates (such as acephate, chlorpyrifos, malathion, diazinon), carbamates (like carbaryl), neonicotinoids (such as imidacloprid, clothianidin), and pyrethroids. Accidental poisoning of beneficial insects often occurs when insecticides drift outside of their target area, when they are applied to blooming crops or weeds, and when bees collect contaminated pollen from plants that do not require bee pollination, such as corn. For information on reducing spray drift and pesticide toxicity, see Appendix D, page 130.

Finally, the introduction of beneficial insects into agricultural settings should always be performed with caution. Predatory biocontrol agents may prey upon beneficial local insects, including pollinators. Similarly the introduction of nonlocal ecotype bees can lead to problems. Just because a bee species is native to an area does not mean that a different strain of the same bee will be native to the area. Nor are the parasites and diseases present on those introduced bees necessarily native to an area. An example of this can be seen with blue orchard bee producers in the Pacific Northwest who ship their bees nationwide. While the blue orchard bee is native to much of the US, only the eastern subspecies, *Osmia lignaria lignaria*, is native east of the Rocky Mountains. The potential ecological consequences of moving the western subspecies *Osmia lignaria propinqua* are

unknown. More practically, nonlocal bees often do not develop in synch with local floral conditions, and often fail to thrive in their new environment.

Pollinator Conservation in Natural and Restored Areas

As with farm settings, pollinator protection in natural areas should begin with macro-level land planning. Old meadows and overgrown pastures tend to have higher pollinator diversity than shaded areas like coniferous woodlands. Conservation efforts for pollinators should focus on areas of present and potential diversity.

Because habitat of this type is now highly fragmented, emphasis should be placed on the construction of corridors to connect otherwise separate natural areas. Pollinators use these corridors to disperse from high-population areas to low-population areas, and to aid genetic diversity by allowing mating between otherwise isolated groups.

Riparian habitat is particularly valuable, as undeveloped riparian vegetation along river corridors can provide hundreds or thousands of miles of continuous habitat. The floodplains of the upper Mississippi River for example are largely free of development, and tributary streams, where they are protected, provide vast "wildlife highways" extending deep into agricultural areas. Where these tributaries meet urban areas, pollinator habitat can be extended with public greenspaces and residential rain gardens (figure 10.6).

Eric Mader

Figure 10.6
This newly established rain garden behind an inner-city factory drains to a local stream and then to a chain of lakes. This creates a wildlife corridor hundreds of miles long that cleans water as it travels through. Attractive signage educates the public and encourages volunteer involvement in ongoing maintenance.

Away from riparian habitat, windbreaks and hedgerows can be used to connect natural areas otherwise separated by agricultural land. In areas of the UK, rural hedgerows are actually protected by law, and are considered an essential link between the nation's remaining woodlands. Windbreaks and hedgerows have the added benefit of reducing wind—many pollinators find it difficult to maneuver in windy locations—and hedgerow plants can often have a high pollen and nectar value to bees.

Projects like hedge planting, shoreline restorations, and construction of rainwater gardens rarely happen in a vacuum. Public involvement should be encouraged, and conservation groups and public agencies should consider pollinators in their planning.

Beyond macro-level land planning, an important stage in habitat conservation for pollinators involves plant selection. This task requires knowledge of what pollinators are native to an area, and an understanding of their lifecycle. If you are lucky, your area may already have high-quality floral sources. Often invasive species like buckthorn or reed canary grass, which crowd out other plants and reduce plant diversity, may need to be removed. In some cases an entirely new plant community may need to be installed.

Because wild pollinators are a diverse group, plant selection should also emphasize diversity (figure 10.7). Plants of diverse flower shapes, colors, and sizes are important because different pollinators often prefer different plants. For example, bumble bees are often attracted to blue and purple flowers, while flies are often found on umbel-type flowers like those in the carrot family. Hummingbirds will be drawn to flowers with deep corollas and abundant nectar, like cardinal flower (*Lobelia cardinalis*), and butterflies may require specific food plants during their caterpillar stage. Ideally restored areas like "bee pastures" or "butterfly gardens" should consist of plants that have overlapping bloom times, so that flowers are present throughout the growing season. Early spring pollen sources like trees and forest ephemerals (delicate, early-blooming understory plants) are especially important for emerging bees, as are late-blooming plants for insects to build energy reserves before winter.

Whenever possible, native "local eco-type" plants should be used, since they are most likely to thrive

Eric Mader

Figure 10.7 Prairie plants provide an attractive border for an urban bike path. A diversity of plants supports a diversity of pollinators.

in a given area. Just because a plant species is native to a site does not mean that it is local eco-type. Commercially produced plants for example may be grown from seed collected hundreds of miles from a planting location. These plants may have emergence patterns or pest and disease problems that differ from plants local to an area. Hybrid and ornamental plants are often not good sources of pollen and nectar, and maintained lawns usually provide no value at all unless "weedy" plants like clover, dandelions, or violets are tolerated.

Of course, if the goal of habitat restoration is to provide a wild reservoir of insects for crop pollination, plants can be selected on the basis of bloom times that occur before or after the crop bloom. Bees and other pollinators can then be expected to move into the crop during flowering and move out when flowering is finished. Through such planning the accidental poisoning of pollinators can be minimized as long as pesticides are not used on the main crop during flowering, and if drift is carefully managed/prevented from affecting adjacent flowering plants (see sidebar, page 112).

In addition to selecting food plants, pollinators also need appropriate habitat for nesting. As with their diverse food requirements, pollinators have diverse nesting requirements. About two-thirds of our native bees nest underground as solitary individuals. Bare patches of well-drained sandy soils are particularly important to these bees. Other bees nest in hollow stems or cavities, such as those created by

Visitors to the Agrecol Corporation's farm south of Madison, Wisconsin are often astounded at what they see—hundreds of acres of native prairie plants growing as row crops. When the big fields of plants like lance-leaved coreopsis (*Coreopsis lanceolata*), or purple prairie clover (*Dalea purpurea)* are in bloom, it is an amazing sight.

HABITAT RESTORATION: A GROWTH INDUSTRY

"Our goal is to produce native seed for habitat restoration," says Agrecol's President Mark Doudlah. "Part of that habitat restoration mission is a commitment to native pollinators. For us, as seed producers, it's a simple equation: no bees equals no seed."

Agrecol, whose name combines "Agriculture" and "Ecology," presents a unique business model, synthesizing native plant production with modern tools like center-pivot irrigation and combine harvesters. Most of the seed Agrecol produces ends up in prairie restoration projects or USDA-sponsored conservation programs like the Conservation Reserve Program (CRP).

Agrecol's farm pollination management consists of a multi-species approach, utilizing managed honey bees and leafcutter bees, as well as habitat conservation for wild bees. These conservation activities include reduced tillage in areas with high populations of ground-nesting bees, night-time pesticide applications to prevent bee poisoning, and an aggressive IPM scouting program that ensures insecticides are only applied when absolutely necessary. The end result is a state-of-the-art farm with a rich diversity of beneficial native insects.

Agrecol's current seed catalog includes over 200 native plant species, many of which are ideal for creating pollinator habitat like bee pastures and butterfly gardens. Custom seed mixes and transplants are also available, and Agrecol even offers installation and maintenance services.

Agrecol Corporation
2918 Agriculture Drive
Madison, WI 53718
Phone: 608-226-2544
www.agrecol.com

Eric Mader

Figure 10.8 Yellow coneflowers grown at Agrecol.

beetle borers in old trees. And bumble bees often nest in tall lodged grasses or abandoned rodent burrows. Dormant wasps, flies, and butterflies have equally diverse habitat requirements.

In addition to the actual nest sites, these pollinators may need construction materials to enhance their nest. Mason bees, which require mud to partition their nests, are classic example of this. For this reason, the more diverse the habitat, the more likely it is to support a diversity of pollinators. Some mixture of different locally appropriate landforms such as wetlands, forests, open meadows, sand dunes, and riparian corridors should be the goal of a diverse pollinator-friendly environment.

Manmade features can also contribute to nest site diversity. Stone walls, piles of field stone or brush, and discarded farm equipment might all be used as nesting sites. Cavity-nesting bees are often found in the walls of abandoned barns and sheds. Even hay bales are sometimes used as nest sites by bumble bees.

Finally, with any conservation project, long-term land management must be considered. Burning and mowing, two common vegetation management tactics, should be exercised with caution. Controlled burns in particular, if performed annually, can devastate populations of dormant pollinators. Performing burns infrequently, and only to small sections of the landscape at a given time may be more appropriate. Mowing should likewise be reduced, and if necessary, should be performed in the fall if possible. If weed encroachment on agricultural land is a concern, often the area directly surrounding fields can be mowed, while other areas are left undisturbed.

Natural areas should also be identified with signage restricting spraying and vehicle traffic, especially off-road vehicles in areas where ground-nesting bees are common.

For long-term preservation, pollinator habitat can be protected with conservation easements and land trusts. These types of land designations can restrict future development and limit the land uses after the owner passes away. Attorneys who specialize in estate planning and real estate issues can draft the documents necessary to establish these protections.

A Managing Parasites and Disease in Solitary Bee Operations

Eric Mader, *Pollinator Outreach Coordinator, the Xerces Society for Invertebrate Conservation*

Leafcutter and mason bees share many of the same enemies. Their parasites and diseases appear with regularity in many operations and can significantly reduce bee numbers unless controlled. The severity of these problems depends upon individual management practices, region, and contamination levels of initial bee stock. Problems can also vary significantly from year to year, even within isolated operations.

Unfortunately, while particular management practices may reduce one problem, they may eventually promote others. For example, loose-cell management facilitates annual nest block cleaning and can significantly reduce chalkbrood contamination. However, unless properly secured, loose bee cells are easily attacked by parasitic wasps.

Sanitation and regular monitoring are essential to maintaining bee health. Fortunately with vigilance, most bee parasites and diseases can be maintained at acceptably low levels. While the following section describes individual parasites and diseases as well as methods for their control, readers should see Appendix G, page 143, for a more comprehensive approach to maintaining bee health.

Wasps

Predatory and parasitic wasps are among the most common enemies of cavity-nesting bees. Most prob-lem species are direct parasites of bees. Using a long, stinger-like ovipositor, these wasp species pierce loose bee cells, cocoons, or unsecured nesting materials, then lay a series of eggs on the bee or bee larva. Upon hatching, the wasp larvae consume the bee.

Chalcid Wasps

Chalcid wasps are among the most destructive parasites of leafcutter and mason bees. This group of wasps includes both native and nonnative species, and has the potential to cause catastrophic losses.

Included in this group are several wasps in the genera *Monodontomerus* (*M. obscurus*, *M. montivaga*, and *M. osmiae*). With the exception of the latter, these species are widespread throughout North America, and all are metallic green, blue, or black, with red eyes and are $5/64$ to $5/32$ inch in length (~2 to 4 millimeters). Males are slightly smaller than females, and emerge slightly earlier through a single hole from the bee cocoon in which they developed.

Female wasps invade nests through small crevices, or through incomplete or uncapped cells. They use their slender, stinger-like ovipositor to paralyze the bee larvae by inserting it through the wall of the cocoon (figure A.1). In some cases they are also capable of inserting the ovipositor through thin mud or leaf cell partitions, or through thin nest materi-

Figure A.1 Adult female chalcid wasp, *Monodontomerus,* ovipositing in blue orchard bee cocoon. Note the long ovipositor at the base of the abdomen.

als such as paper straws or cardboard tubes less than $3/64$ inch thick (~1 millimeter). They are extremely opportunistic and will invade the innermost cells of nests when possible. Unprotected loose cells are attacked mercilessly, and each female may attack multiple cells. Bees are susceptible to attack up to one day before hatching.

After paralyzing the bee larva, the female *Monodontomerus* lays a series of eggs (averaging 10, but up to 50) between the host larva and the inner wall of the cocoon. Upon hatching, the wasp larvae consume the bee and then pupate within the bee cocoon for up to a month. The typical sex ratio of the offspring is highly female (3:1). Because of their rapid development time and high numbers of female progeny, multiple generations can occur each season, and population growth can be explosive.

More common than *Monodontomerus* in many leafcutter bee operations is another chalcid wasp, *Pteromalus venustus.* This wasp is native to Europe and may have arrived in North America with the alfalfa leafcutter bee.

The size of *P. venustus* is similar to the *Monodontomerus* wasps with females averaging up to $7/64$ inch (~2.5 millimeters) long. Females are black with dark brown legs. Males are the same, but have a metallic green head. *P. venustus* is believed to have a higher reproductive capacity than other chalcids, and over 100 eggs have been observed on a single bee larva—usually fewer are present however. Larvae are about $7/64$ inch (~2.5 millimeters) long at maturity, white,

and hairless (as opposed to *Monodontomerus* larvae which are covered with small bristles). Development is similar to that of *Monodontomerus* with larvae either progressing to adulthood, or overwintering as mature larvae. Multiple generations occur in a single season, and occasionally several generations will even occur during incubation of leafcutter bee cells resulting in high losses.

Melittobia chalybii is another chalcid wasp species, which not only parasitizes cavity-nesting bees, but many other bee and wasp species as well—including bumble bees. However, this native parasite is less common than *P. venustus* or *Monodontomerus* wasps. As with the previously discussed chalcids, the adults of this species are brown or black in color, and measure about $5/64$ inch (2 millimeters) in length. A notable difference is that both winged and wingless males have been described.

Mating among *M. chalybii* occurs within the parasitized cocoon, where males remain. Mature larvae are about $3/64$ inch (~1 millimeter) long, about half the length of mature Monodontomerus or *P. venustus* larvae. Egg laying and development is similar to other chalcid wasps. Multiple generations occur in a single season, with some larvae overwintering.

Unlike *P. venustus*, or *Monodontomerus*, *M. chalybii* gains access to host bee larvae by chewing holes through cocoons and nest partitions. Light traps are considered ineffective for the control of this parasite, and males have even been described as blind. Despite this, populations of *M. chalybii* are normally low in most beekeeping operations, and the parasite reportedly does not survive well under prolonged artificial cold storage conditions.

Another less common chalcid parasite is *Dibrachys confusus.* The size and coloration of this wasp is similar to that of *P. venustus*, however the legs of *D. confusus* are red, orange, or yellow. As with *P. venustus*, *D. confusus* emerge from a single hole in the parasitized cell (with males emerging first), then mating occurs. Ovipositing and development are similar to other chalcids. Multiple generations may occur in a single season, and the sex ratio is more male based than other chalcids (2:1). Although *D. confusus* has been identified as a parasite of the alfalfa leafcutter bee, it seems to be of minor importance. Higher parasitism levels occur on native leafcutter bee species, such as

Megachile relativa. Its occurrence among mason bees is unknown.

Chalcid wasps overwinter as mature larvae (figure A.2) and emerge in leafcutter bee incubators (figure A.3) over several days—beginning on day 9 at 86°F (30°C) and continuing until day 14 (see sidebar, page 91). Several control measures exist, but the most important practice is the use of solid nesting materials free of entry points, particularly in the rear of the nest. For this reason, drilled boards and Styrofoam nest blocks should have a tight-fitting backing material. Nests should also be removed from the field promptly after the nesting period to reduce exposure. Stored nest materials and loose cocoons can be covered with a 1-inch (2.54-centimeter) thick layer of sawdust or vermiculite (not perlite) to minimize parasite movement. Bee storage areas and incubators should be equipped with a light trap consisting of an ultraviolet black light suspended over a pan of water. Several drops of detergent should be added to the water to reduce surface tension. As wasps emerge from the nest materials, they are attracted to the light, where they fall into the water and drown. Many chalcid wasps are poor fliers, preferring to hop, so light traps should be placed on the floor of the storage area or incubator.

Nest materials and loose cocoons can also be protected by surrounding stored bees with yellow sticky cards (the kind used for monitoring crop pests), or with a fine mesh screen, or even several layers of pantyhose. Care should be taken so that contaminated materials are not confined with clean materials. Vacuuming the storage area walls and floors is also an important control tactic, especially during incubation.

Canadian leafcutter producers control chalcid wasps with dichlorvos resin pest strips (such as Vapona™) during bee incubation. This treatment is applied from days 9 to 12 of the incubation process, after which the incubator is ventilated to remove all remaining vapor. Dichlorvos is not labeled for this purpose in the US, and improper use can result in high bee mortality. It is not recommended.

Finally, small batches of mason bee cocoons can be hand sorted to remove chalcid wasps. Parasitized cocoons are often less firm than normal cocoons and appear almost empty when squeezed lightly (figure A.4). Questionable cocoons can be segregated and held in a transparent plastic container with a tight fitting lid. The container can then be checked several times a day and emerging wasps discarded.

Among the largest chalcid wasp parasites is *Leucospis affinis*, a native species measuring up to almost ½ inch in length (12.7 millimeters). This species is readily identified by its distinct black and yellow color pattern, and is easily spotted around field shelters and nest blocks where it parasitizes both leafcutter and mason bees. *L. affinis* parasitizes the pre-pupal stages of its host and has an extremely long ovipositor (normally folded over the abdomen) capable of piercing wood up to ¾ inch or 19 millimeters (figure A.5). Because of this, paper, cardboard, and Styrofoam nest materials are easily attacked—as are drilled wooden blocks with nest tunnels located near

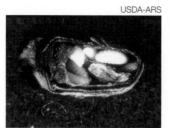

Figure A.2
Chalcid wasp larvae inside a leafcutter bee cell.

Figure A.3
Leafcutter bee cocoon with exiting chalcid wasp (*Monodontomerus*).

Figure A.4 Infested blue orchard bee cocoon opened to show *Monodontomerus* larvae.

Figure A.5 *Leucospis affinis* ovipositing into a leafcutter bee nest.

the edge of the block. A single generation occurs per year, with a single wasp developing per cell (which overwinters as a prepupa).

Aside from promptly removing and securely storing nest materials at the end of the season, few control measures exist for *L. affinis*. Loose-cell management does not provide effective control in many instances because wasp prepupae remain enclosed within the host cocoon, making identification and physical separation difficult. Fortunately the low reproductive rate of this parasite prevents it from becoming problematic in most instances.

Various other chalcid wasp parasites of cavity-nesting bees, such as *Tetrastichus megachilids*, exist, but few of these lesser-known species are commonly encountered in populations of managed bees.

Sapygid Wasps

Sapygid wasps are cleptoparasites of both leafcutter and mason bees. Cleptoparasitic insects do not directly prey upon their host species, but rather consume the food provision of the host, killing it in the process. A number of these sapygid species are associated with solitary bees, including *Sapyga martini, S. centrata,* and *S. pumila*. Adults are typically black and yellow and measure up to about ½ inch long (12.7 millimeters).

Sapygid wasps lay their eggs in the nests of bees while the female bee is away foraging. Several eggs may be laid, although only one offspring develops. This offspring kills the developing bee and any sapygid siblings, and then feeds on the pollen-nectar pro-

vision. The larva undergoes several growth stages before spinning a cocoon and pupating. The wasp then overwinters as an adult, with a single generation per year.

S. pumila is commonly associated with leafcutter bees in some areas, and has been found to spend the night inside the holes of bee nest blocks. However, when available, *S. pumila* prefers smaller holes, $^3/_{32}$ inch (~2.5 millimeter) in diameter, and various traps have been devised to take advantage of that habit. These "night station traps" often consist of a section of PVC pipe, closed on both ends and drilled with a series of $^3/_{32}$-inch holes. Within the pipe section, a length of flypaper, pesticide-impregnated cardboard, or a strip of sticky cardboard (such as yellow sticky cards used for monitoring crop pests), is inserted. Alternate sapygid trap designs have been developed, consisting of black-light attractants with a series of passageways that separate insects by size—drowning the smaller sapygids in a pan of oil, and allowing the larger bees to escape. Such traps are not in widespread use however.

Chrysidid Wasps

A number of chrysidid wasps prey upon solitary bees; these include *Chrysura smaragdicolor* and *C. pacifica* in the western, and *C. kyae* in the eastern states. All are minor native predators measuring up to about ½ inch in length (12.7 millimeters), and are typically metallic green in color (figure A.6).

Female chysidids lay their eggs in unattended bee nests (while the female bee is away). Upon hatching,

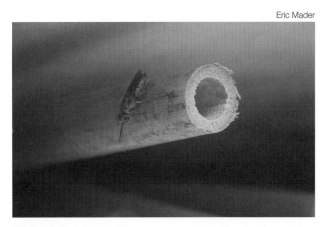

Figure A.6 A female *Chrysura* sp. wasp waiting for its opportunity to lay eggs in a bee nest.

the wasp larva attaches itself to the host larva which it later consumes. After feeding, the wasp larva then spins a thin, semi-transparent cocoon before overwintering. *Chrysura* wasps overwinter as adults, and there is one generation a year.

Ichneumon Wasps

This group of solitary wasps consists of two families, the Ichneumonidae and the Braconidae. Together they comprise nearly 100,000 diverse species worldwide, ranging in size from ⅛ inch to over 5 inches (~3 to 130 millimeters) in length. As with other parasitic wasps, ichneumons pierce natal bee nests and lay one or more eggs on the developing bee.

The vast majority of wasps in this group do not prey upon bees, but instead are beneficial biological controls of many pest insects. However, the large size of some ichneumons, along with their occasionally alarming appearance (with some individuals bearing ovipositors over an inch in length), can cause concern when they are observed ovipositing into sealed bee nests.

Normally control can be achieved simply by removing nests from the field promptly after they are filled and storing them in a secure indoor location. Styrofoam leafcutter nests tend to be the most easily attacked by these wasps, though many species can oviposit through solid wood.

Other Predatory Wasps

Large Vespid wasps such as the German yellowjacket (*Vespula germanica*), the bald-faced hornet (*Dolichovespula maculate*), and paper wasps (in the genus *Polistes*), are occasional minor predators of managed bees. These wasps form conspicuous paper nests and live together in social units much like ants or honey bees.

Adult wasps feed on carbohydrate sources such as flower nectar, and prey upon insects as a protein source for their developing offspring. Usually no control is necessary. However, occasionally these wasps may construct hives near mason bee nests, or even within leafcutter bee shelters. In these cases predation levels may be high.

Routine inspection of bee shelters should be performed, and wasp nests should be removed as necessary. Pesticide use should be avoided so as to avoid bee poisoning. Protective clothing, including a honey beekeeper's veil and gloves should be worn when removing wasp nests. Occasionally wasps will attempt to rebuild new nests in place of the removed one, so follow-up inspections are necessary.

Mites

Currently, most mite problems involving cavity-nesting bees are associated with the so-called hairy-fingered mite (*Chaetodactylus krombeini*), a major native cleptoparasite of the blue orchard bee (figure A.7). A related species, *Chaetodactylus nipponicus*, is considered a major pest of the hornfaced bee in Japan where it is blamed for 80 percent of all bee mortality, and annual yield losses of up to 30 percent, without treatment. Various mite species have also been associated with the alfalfa leafcutter bee, but little published information exists. Mites are not considered a major threat to leafcutter bee operations at this time due to the common practice of loose-cell management.

The hairy-fingered mite, sometimes called a pollen mite, is most commonly reported in humid climates, especially in coastal regions. The mites are typically white, yellow, or red, and are at first difficult to discern from individual pollen grains when viewing an infested nest.

Pavel Klimov

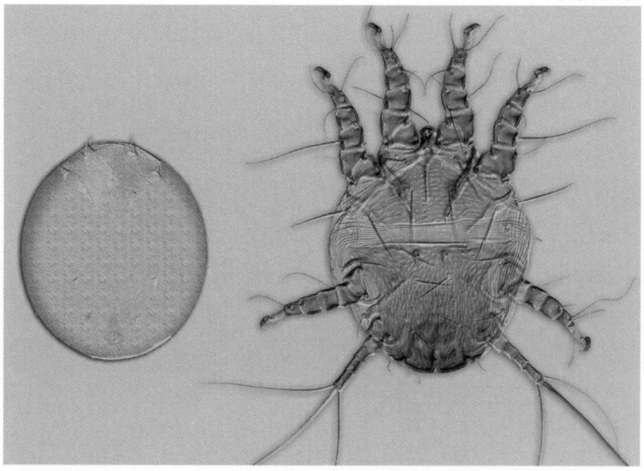

Figure A.7 Nonmigratory (left), and migratory (right) stages of the hairy-fingered mite (*Chaetodactylus krombeini*).

Immature hairy-fingered mites feed on the pollen provisions within nest tubes, causing the developing bee to starve, and in some cases mites may even feed on the bee larva itself. Multiple generations can occur within an infested cell in a single season—a single mite for example can give rise to thousands of offspring packed into a single cell space. When such nests are opened and the contents shaken onto a surface, the movement of individual mites is soon noticed. Since the mites cannot break through the mud wall partitions of mason bee nests, they remain confined throughout most of the season.

Upon emergence, bees nesting deeper within the cavity are forced to climb through mite-infested cells. During this process, a migratory stage of the mite with long bristle-like legs (hence the common name), attaches itself to the thorax of the healthy bee (figure A.8). Large numbers of these migratory nymphs can in some cases actually hinder the flight of emerging bees, although they do not directly attack adult bees.

During nesting, these mites are transported by the bees to newly provisioned cavities where the cycle repeats itself. Although adult bees will groom themselves to remove mites, it is difficult to completely eradicate them in a population once they are established (figure A.9).

Effective control measures include annual phase-out and cleaning of old nest materials, and the disposal of contaminated nests. With high infestations, cocoons can be removed (loose-cell management), and submerged in a bleach-water solution (1:3 by volume) for about five minutes.

Figure A.8 A blue orchard bee with hairy-fingered mites attached to the thorax.

Figure A.9 An *Osmia lignaria* nest tube split lengthwise to reveal a hairy-fingered mite infestation. The orange mites have completely consumed the cell contents.

Japanese mason beekeepers have developed two control measures for *Chaetodactylus* mites: The first method involves heat treatment of hornfaced bee pre-pupae in late June, after cocoon spinning. Pre-pupae, which reportedly tolerate high heat at this stage, are exposed to temperatures of 86°F (30°C) for 30 to 40 days. Because the bees are in summer diapause they have little mortality, but the mites that are still active are killed.

The second Japanese control method involves treatment of nest materials with 60 ppm of the insecticide endosulfan (sold under the trade names Thiodan, Endocide, Beosit, Cyclodan, Malix, Thimul, and Thifor in the US). Bamboo or reed nests are dip-treated prior to the nesting season with this method, or alternatively nest entrances are sometimes sprayed every two or three days during the nesting season. Note that no endosulfan product is currently labeled for this use in the US, and improper endosulfan applications will likely result in bee mortality.

Hairy-fingered mites, along with the fungal disease chalkbrood, are two reasons why untended drilled nest blocks should not be used to "encourage wild bee populations."

Cuckoo Bees

Cuckoo bees, like sapygid wasps and hairy-fingered mites, are cleptoparasites. Female cuckoo bees lay a single egg in the uncapped cell of the host bee while the rightful owner is away foraging. Upon hatching, the parasite larva kills the host and consumes its food provision. There is a single generation per year and the development timeline closely matches that of the host bee.

In most instances cuckoo bees closely resemble their host species, typically only lacking the pollen-collecting scopal hairs on the underside of the abdomen. Cuckoo bees often belong to the same family as their host, in this case, the family Megachilidae.

Four species in the genus *Coelioxys* are sometimes associated with alfalfa leafcutter bees: *funeraria, gilensis, sodalis,* and *moesta.* All of these species tend to be less common in prairie regions. Each species resembles other leafcutter bees, except females tend to have a longer, more sharply pointed abdomen, and males have a broader abdomen. Females and males of each species have short distinct spines protruding from the last segment (figure A.10).

Female *Coelioxys* can sometimes be recognized near nest blocks by their rapid flight movements as they attempt to enter nesting holes during active leafcutter foraging. Eggs are laid either in exposed pollen provisions, or by ovipositing through the leaf lining into the pollen mass. Five instars occur, with the third instar usually killing the host or other cuckoo bee larvae. The development cycle is similar to leafcutter bees (see figure 7.10, page 80), although these cuckoo species tend to emerge before the alfalfa leafcutter bees during incubation. For this reason, light traps during incubation can be an effective control measure to reduce *Coelioxys* populations.

Stelis montana (figure A.11), another cleptoparasite, is commonly associated with the blue orchard bee. As with other cuckoo bees this species closely resembles its host in color and appearance. Distinguishing characteristics include a slightly smaller body, a lack of white facial hairs, and the absence of a pollen-collecting scopa. The lifecycle of *S. montana* mirrors that of other cuckoo bees with the female laying an egg in the host bee's nest while it is away. *Stelis* eggs are about two-thirds the size of *Osmia* eggs. *Stelis* larvae kill and consume the host larva along with the pollen-nectar provision. Unlike the blue orchard

Figure A.11 *Stelis montana,* a cleptoparasitic (or "cuckoo") bee, superficially resembles its host, the blue orchard bee.

bee, *Stelis montana* overwinters in the pre-pupal stage inside a silk cocoon. Development continues the following spring with emergence occurring near the end of the blue orchard bee nesting period. Because of its later emergence and nesting period, the majority of parasitized cells are outermost male cells of the blue orchard bee. *Stelis* cocoons can be identified when compared to blue orchard bee cocoons by their prominent nipple on one end, and the presence of long curly fecal pellets. For this reason, they can be hand sorted when cocoons are managed as loose cells, or identified and removed in translucent paper nest straws that are viewed against a strong light.

Various other lesser-known cuckoo bees exist. The genus *Dioxys* includes many cleptoparasites of various leafcutter and mason bee species, and the genus *Nomada* includes cleptoparasites of the ground-nesting alkali bee (*Nomia melanderi*).

Beetles

Beetles constitute the most diverse insect order on Earth. The vast majority of them are beneficial, preying on crop pests and recycling nutrients. Only a few of them present challenges to beekeepers.

Blister Beetles

Various species of blister beetles (in the beetle family Meloidae) are common cleptoparasites of many cavity-nesting bees. *Tricrania stansburyi,* measures up to about ½ inch (12.7 millimeters) long as an adult and is black with red wing covers (figure A.12). Adults of *Nemognatha lutea* and *N. vittigera,*

Figure A.10
Coelioxys sp., the cuckoo bees of the alfalfa leafcutter bee, can be identified by their sharply pointed abdomens ending in several distinct spines.

Figure A.12 Adult blister beetle, *Tricrania stansburyi*.

Figure A.14 Wintering adult blister beetle, *Tricrania stansburyi*, enclosed within its cocoon-like coarctate

Figure A.13 Adult brown blister beetle, *Nemognathus vittigera*.

commonly called brown blister beetles, are the same size but are yellow or brown in color (figure A.13).

Both beetles have similar lifecycles, with females laying their eggs in large masses on the buds and flowers of many common weedy plants. Upon hatching, the first larval stage (called a triungulin) crawls to the top of the flower and waits for visiting bees. Using claw-studded legs, the triungulins grasp the hairs of visiting bees and are transported back to the nest cavity where they detach themselves. Within the sealed nest, the beetle larva consumes the pollen-nectar provision and the bee egg. Within mason bee nests, beetle larval movement is normally restricted by the mud partitions. However, within leafcutter bee nests, beetle larvae may move between cells, destroying several in the process.

Development occurs rapidly, and the beetles overwinter either as adults or as pupae. There is a single generation per year, and overwintering beetles are encased within a semi-translucent brown cocoon-like skin called a coarctate (figure A.14). Loose-cell management of bees allows for the effective separation of bee cocoons and coarctate. Tumbling of bee cells also destroys beetle coarctate, by rupturing

the outer membrane causing desiccation. Without control, adult beetles emerge the following spring. Blister beetles are more common in areas with abundant wildflowers than in regions that are intensively farmed.

Checkered Flower Beetles

Another major cleptoparasite of cavity-nesting bees are the checkered flower beetles, *Trichodes ornatus* and *T. nutalli*. Adult beetles measure just over ½ inch in length (12.7 millimeters) and are dark blue with yellow, orange, or red spotted patterns on their wing covers (figures A.15 and A.16).

Female beetles lay their eggs near the entrances of bee nests. Upon hatching, the first several larval stages (which are white or pink, and up to ½ inch long) move between nest cavities consuming pollen provisions as well as bee eggs. Larval stages can be recognized by their grub-like appearance and the

Figure A.15 Adult checkered flower beetle, *Trichodes nutalli,* resting on a sunflower.

Figure A.16 Adult checkered flower beetle, *Trichodes ornatus.*

Managing Parasites and Disease in Solitary Bee Operations   121

Figure A.17 Checkered flower beetle, *Trichodes ornatus,* fully grown larva. Note forked spiny process at the tip of the abdomen (left).

two prominent spines protruding from the tip of the abdomen (figure A.17). There is typically one generation per year, with the fourth larval stage overwintering inside a coarctate.

The checkered flower beetle has been associated with both mason bees and leafcutter bees, and pheromone traps have been employed as a control measure among some leafcutter beekeepers. Leafcutter operations in the Pacific Northwest have been most affected, while beekeepers in prairie regions generally have a lower incidence of beetles. As with many parasites, mason beekeepers can avoid most checkered flower beetle damage by promptly removing nests from the field at the end of the nesting period.

Stored-Product Beetles

Various stored-product beetles are commonly associated with leafcutter and mason bee operations. They include carpet beetles (*Trogoderma glabra, T. variabile, Anthrenus verbasci, Attagenus* spp., and *Megatoma* spp.); the red, black and confused flour beetles (*Tribolium castaneum, T. audox,* and *T. confusum*); the sawtoothed and rusty grain beetles (*Oryzaephilus surinamensis,* and *Cryptolestes ferrugineus*); various spider beetles (*Ptinus* spp.); and several beetles without common names, including *Tribolium brevicornis* and *Tenebroides maurtanicus.*

Larval and adult stages of these beetles are attracted to pollen provisions and are most common in poorly constructed nests or around facilities where grain and seed products are stored. Most are capable of feeding at low temperatures and often have a high reproductive rate with multiple generations per year. Because of this, they may be found in field shelters, nests, incubators, and storage facilities. Sanitation is a critical control factor.

Among the spider beetles, *Ptinus californicus* has been cited as a common pest in some areas. This beetle lays its eggs within the unsealed cells of bee nests where several larvae may develop, feeding on the pollen provision and in the process starving or injuring the immature bee.

Adult spider beetles are brown with linear white patches on the wing covers, have long antennae, and measure up to about $3/16$ inch (~5 millimeters) in length. There is typically one generation per year with adult or larval stages overwintering within the bee nest inside a coarctate. Infested cells are characterized by an abundance of long stringy feces, and sometimes-ragged emergence holes, where adult beetles have exited. Loose-cell management and nesting systems that facilitate cocoon inspection (such as paper straws or laminate boards) are the primary method of control.

The smooth carpet beetle (*Trogoderma glabra*), another common nest scavenger, has a similar feeding habit. As with other stored-product beetles, adults lay their eggs inside unsealed nest cells. Broken or incomplete cell partitions further facilitate larval movement between cells and egg laying by adults.

Carpet beetles usually measure less than ⅛ inch in length (~3 millimeters), are mottled brown, black, tan, and white, and are roughly oval shaped (similar to lady beetles). Larvae may reach almost $3/16$ inch in length (~5 millimeters) and are often brown or orange in color and covered with bristles. Multiple generations a year are common.

Flour beetles are a similar size to spider and carpet beetles, $3/16$ to $15/64$ inch in length (~5 to 6 millimeters). However, adults are usually more stout in appearance, are often brown in color, and have deep groove patterns running lengthwise along the wing covers. The larval stages often have distinct light and dark segmented bodies, with short spine-like protrusions at the tip of the abdomen.

Flies

Two fly species are occasional minor predators of leafcutter and mason bees. The larvae of the dewy bee fly (*Anthrax irroratus*) are occasionally found feeding on immature bees. Two spikes projecting from the head of the immature fly are used to break through cell partitions.

Physocephala texana, a conopid fly, briefly lands upon foraging adult bees and deposits an egg through the bee's abdominal intersegmental membrane. The egg hatches, and the larva consumes the bee from the inside out. Adult bees killed by this fly are recognized by an elongated abdomen containing the fly pupa. No known control measures exist for either fly species.

Moths

The driedfruit moth (*Vitula edmandsae*), and the indianmeal moth (*Plodia interpunctella*) are two destructive scavengers sometimes associated with cavity-nesting bees. Both cause damage in their larval stage by feeding on nectar-pollen provisions and bee larvae. In the process of tunneling between cells, the moth larva may destroy multiple cocoons, and may even chew through the walls of Styrofoam nests. Fecal pellets, massive amounts of silk webbing, and cast skins are typical signs of infestation.

Driedfruit moth adults have a wingspan of about ¾ inch (19 millimeters), and are light grey with irregular grey wing markings. Females typically live up to 20 days as adults, with males only living around 10 days. Mating occurs shortly after adult emergence, and females lay up to 325 eggs beginning three days later. The cream-colored eggs are often laid in cracks and crevices around bee nests, and hatch within four to six days.

Nest invasion occurs through uncapped tunnels and along the sides of nest blocks that are drilled all the way through. From there, larvae move between nest tunnels via the back of the nest block. The larvae pass through five or six instars over a 30-day period. As it feeds, a moth larva constructs a silk-like webbed tunnel, and when disturbed will retreat into this webbing. Upon maturity the moth larvae often exit the nest and congregate in webbed clusters of up to several hundred individuals, usually located in the back or corners of nest shelters. Pupation lasts for about eleven days, and several generations can occur in a single year.

Indianmeal moth adults are reddish-brown with a metallic sheen over most of their wings, which span about ⅝ inch (~16 millimeters). Their body length is typically ½ inch (12.7 millimeters). Females may lay up to 400 eggs, with a lifecycle nearly identical to that of the driedfruit moth. Damage is also nearly identical to that of the driedfruit moth, and is also accompanied by feces and silk webbing. In fact, distinguishing between immature stages of the two species can be difficult for a layperson.

Control measures for both moths include tumbling of loose cells to remove moth pupae and the use of light traps during bee incubation. If nest blocks are drilled all the way through, the backing material should be held securely in place. Pheromone traps, which can be used for control of minor infestations, are also commercially available.

Earwigs

Earwigs are a common nuisance associated with solitary bee nests in the eastern US. In particular, the introduced European Earwig (*Forficula auricularia*), is commonly observed in humid areas where it scavenges in and around bee nest tubes during the summer—often eating pollen provisions, leaf nest materials, and sometimes bee eggs. Despite their appearance, the large pinchers located at the base of the abdomen are mostly harmless, although earwigs will bare them in a defensive posture if threatened (figure A.18).

Earwigs can fly, but rarely do. They usually gain entry to free-standing nest shelters by crawling up the shelter legs, or via vegetation leaning against

Cedar Creek Nature Center

Figure A.18
European earwigs, *Forficula auriclaria*, are common opportunistic nest destroyers in many parts of the Eastern US.

the shelter. Control is achieved by coating the shelter legs with a layer of automotive grease or a sticky insect barrier such as Tanglefoot™.

Ants

Like earwigs, ants are an occasional minor nuisance to mason and leafcutter bees. Damage is usually restricted to newly laid exposed bee eggs. Once nests are sealed, ant damage is usually minimal. Fire ants (*Solenopsis invicta*) and Argentine ants (*Linepithema humile*) have both been cited as nuisances, although many other species may also cause problems. Control is the same as for earwigs.

Chalkbrood

The single most destructive disease of cavity-nesting bees is the fungal pathogen chalkbrood. Several chalkbrood species exist, including *Ascosphaera torchioi* (affecting mason bees), *A. larvis,* and *A. aggrerata* (both affecting the alfalfa leafcutter bee). These pathogens are different from the chalkbrood disease affecting honey bees (*Ascophaera apis*).

Chalkbrood kills the bee by infecting the gut where it competes with the larva for food, resulting in starvation. As the disease progresses, a fungal mass (called mycelium), consisting of individual filaments (called hyphae) are produced. They penetrate the gut wall, and consume the remainder of the larval body. At the end of the individual hyphae, spores are produced in a sack-like structure called an asci.

These spore-filled asci often remain just below the skin surface of the infested cadaver, and along with the mycelial mass, give the dead larva a chalky, discolored appearance ranging from brown to grey, black, or white—depending on the stage of fungal development (figure A.19).

Eric Mader

Figure A.19 A bamboo Osmia nest tube split lengthwise to reveal chalkbrood cadavers in the innermost cells.

Chalkbrood fungi are related to many common plant pathogens such as apple scab (*Venturia inaequalis*) and powdery mildews. As with those plant diseases, chalkbrood spores are common in the environment and may be picked up from flowers by adult bees while foraging. As those adults return to the nest, the spores may contaminate the pollen-nectar provision. Larvae consume those spores, which germinate inside the gut. The disease cycle is further compounded when emerging bees chew through those contaminated nest cells and cadavers (which may contain millions of spores) while exiting the nest. Those emerging bees in turn provision new cells, which are also contaminated with the disease. The resulting epidemic can produce dramatic losses, and leafcutter beekeepers in the Pacific Northwest have routinely seen population losses in excess of 50 percent. Because of this disease, most leafcutter bee production has shifted to Canada where disease pressure is lower and treatments that are not permitted in the US (such as paraformaldehyde fumigation) are allowed.

The only effective control measure for chalkbrood in the US is constant, vigilant sanitation! Nest materials for leafcutter and mason bees should be phased out annually. Previously used nest materials should not be used unless thoroughly disinfected by submerging in a bleach-water solution (1:3 by volume) for five minutes. Wood nesting materials can also be sanitized by kiln drying in small lumber kilns.

Loose-cell management has been touted as an effective method of controlling chalkbrood, and the process does facilitate annual nest block cleaning. However, infected cells that are tumbled with clean cells also have the potential to spread spores. To combat this, some bee producers submerge cells for one minute in a bleach-water solution. If loose cells are not used, a phaseout system should be employed to prevent bees from re-nesting in the previous season's nests. In addition, field shelters, incubation trays, and other beekeeping equipment should be cleaned annually.

Other factors can increase chalkbrood incidence. These include stress, second-generation bees, nest crowding, high moisture levels, and cool temperatures. Wherever possible these factors should be minimized. Both the leafcutter and mason bee chapters discuss these management issues.

Birds and Rodents

Birds of several species prey upon both adult and dormant bees. Starlings, robins, various swallows, summer tanagers, and the eastern kingbird have all been observed feeding upon newly emerged adult bees. Woodpeckers may also cause significant damage to both bee larvae and nest materials (figure A.20). Once birds recognize bee nests as a source of food, they are difficult to deter.

Chicken wire of the largest available mesh will protect bee shelters from intrusion, but will also deter nesting bees. Metal mesh in particular tends to damage bee wings, and bees have difficulty navigating in and out of the mesh, especially when many bees are present. It should therefore only be used when absolutely necessary (after bird damage has occurred). When using chicken wire, the distance between the mesh and the nesting materials is critical to minimize problems. Ideally, the mesh should be no more than 3 to 4 inches (7.6 to 10 centimeters) from the surface of nest blocks. Closer placement does not protect against bird beaks, and further distances disrupt bee flight significantly.

Eric Mader

Figure A.20 A styrofoam leafcutter nest block damaged by woodpeckers.

Rodents such as chipmunks, mice, and squirrels cause similar problems. As with birds, nest shelters can be secured with mesh as necessary, and free-standing shelter legs can be coated with automotive grease or Tanglefoot™. Care should also be taken to protect stored nest blocks from rodents. Styrofoam nests in particular are easily destroyed by mice, which are attracted to pollen provisions and dormant bees.

B X-Ray Proceedures for Cavity-Nesting Bees

Eric Mader, *Pollinator Outreach Coordinator, the Xerces Society for Invertebrate Conservation*

Inspection of dormant cavity-nesting bees and bee larvae is a difficult process. For example, dormant adult mason bees inside reed or cardboard nest tubes cannot be inspected without splitting the tube lengthwise. Once revealed, the cocoons themselves often provide few clues as to the condition of the bees within. Loose cocoons must be sacrificed to dissection via scalpel.

Similarly, leafcutter prepupae are difficult to examine within their individual leaf cells. The presence of chalkbrood-infested individuals, parasites, and "pollen balls"—dud cells containing no live bee—can be a challenge to ascertain.

Fortunately, X-ray analysis can provide an effective way to check the condition of immature bees without requiring dissection, surgical tools, or a microscope. Performed properly, X-ray inspection is not harmful to bees, and does not require the disassembly of individual mason bee nest tubes. However, bees nesting in drilled block-type nests must be removed so that individual cocoons or leafcutter cells can be examined.

Standard mammography or industrial X-ray machines like the cabinet-type Hewlett-Packard Faxitron model 43804n (or model 43855A) are currently used by labs performing analysis of leafcutter bees. Local veterinarians may also have suitable equipment.

Voltage settings of 20 to 25 Kv with a current of 2.0 ma for 30 to 60 seconds on medium grain indus-

trial film (such as Kodak Industrex M) provide good images of dormant mason bees (within natal nest tubes) and individual leafcutter larvae.

When viewed during larval development stages, sampled bees should be a consistent size and shape (figure B.1). Most types of parasites and nest destroyers should be readily apparent upon inspection. Dormant adult mason bees, such as BOBs, should have a white abdomen in fall and winter indicating stored fat reserves. Black abdomens indicate depleted energy that may have resulted from bees being stored in overly warm conditions (greater than 40°F, ~5°C).

University of Idaho, SW Idaho Research and Extension Center

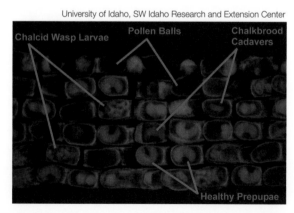

Figure B.1 A close-up X-ray image of leafcutter cells. Pollen balls appear as black cells. Chalkbrood cadavers are often darker, smaller, or misshapen. Chalcid wasp larvae, which have already consumed the immature bee, are observed as a mass of small individuals.

C Plants for Bee Ranching

Eric Mader, *Pollinator Outreach Coordinator, the Xerces Society for Invertebrate Conservation*

A bee pasture is managed for plants that maximize bee reproduction ("bee ranching"). This is a different goal from habitat conservation or honey production. To be effective a pasture must provide an abundant bloom throughout the nesting period—especially in the early stages of bee emergence. In many cases companion planting is necessary. For example, the floor of a cherry orchard could be planted with vetch or clover to provide ongoing floral sources for mason bees. Similarly, buckwheat is often planted near leafcutter bee shelters in alfalfa fields as a source of cut leaves for nest construction.

The table on page 128 includes a variety of plants that are suitable for large-scale bee ranching organized by bloom period. Many of these plants have value in their own right as silage, oilseed, fruit, or cover crops.

Table C.1
Plants that are Suitable for Large-Scale Bee Ranching

CROP	SCIENTIFIC NAME	NATIVE	TYPE	BLOOM PERIOD	HEIGHT[1]	SOWING SEASON	SOW PER[1] 1000 SQ. FT.	SOW PER[1] ACRE	SOIL INOCULANT REQUIRED?	COMMENTS
Pussy willow	*Salix* spp.	Yes	Tree	Early spring	5–15 ft.	Anytime	5–10 ft. spacing	5–10 ft. spacing	No	Excellent early pollen source for emerging spring bees. European species may be better than native.
Siberian squill	*Scilla siberica*	No	Perennial	Early spring	6 in.	Fall	Bulbs spaced 10 in.	Bulbs spaced 10 in.	No	Very early blooming shade plant. Good forage source for mason bees.
Cherry	*Prunus* spp.	Both	Tree	Early spring	5–100 ft.	Anytime	Depends on species	Depends on species	No	Avoid sterile ornamental varieties.
Meadow-foam	*Limnanthes alba*	Yes	Annual	Spring	10–18 in.	Fall	2 lb.	25 lb.	No	A less common oilseed crop. Excellent for mason bees.
Rapeseed	*Brassica napus*	No	Annual	Spring	3–5 ft.	Spring or Fall	4 oz.	4–10 lb.	No	Prolific bloom. Good nectar source.
Oilseed radish	*Raphanus sativus*	No	Annual	Spring–summer	2–3 ft.	Spring	1 lb.	25 lb.	No	Avoid planting in rotation with cole crops due to shared pests and diseases.
Blueberry	*Vaccinium* spp.	Yes	Shrub	Spring–summer	1–15 ft.	Anytime	5–10 ft. spacing	5–10 ft. spacing	No	Good forage source for many bee species.
Crimson clover	*Trifolium incarnatum*	No	Annual	Spring–summer	18 in.	Fall or Spring	1–2 lb.	20–30 lb.	Yes	Excellent cover crop. Cold-hardy winter annual.
Smooth penstemon	*Penstemon digitalis*	Yes	Perennial	Spring–summer	1–3 ft.	Fall	5 oz.	2 lb.	No	Commonly associated with various mason bees in the upper Mississippi River valley.
Early figwort	*Scrophularia lanceolata*	Yes	Perennial	Spring–summer	3–7 ft.	Fall	1 oz.	4 lb.	No	Short bloom period, extremely prolific nectar producer.
Phacelia	*Phacelia tanacetifolia*	Yes	Annual	Spring–summer	2–3 ft.	Spring	4–8 oz.	5–10 lb.	No	One of the best bee pasture plants.
Borage	*Borago officinalis*	No	Annual	Spring–summer	1–4 ft.	Fall	4–8 oz.	5–10 lb.	No	Very prolific bloom. Good pollen, and excellent nectar source.
Kura clover	*Trifolium ambiguum*	No	Perennial	Spring–summer	10 in.	Fall	0.5 lb.	6–10 lb.	Yes	Good choice for apple orchards. Provides minor apple scab suppression.
Hairy vetch	*Vicia villosa*	No	Annual	Spring–summer	2–3 ft.	Fall	1–2 lb.	20–30 lb.	Yes	Good for cold climates.

Common name	Scientific name		Life cycle	Bloom	Height	Planting	Rate (drilled)	Rate (broadcast)		Notes
Strawberry clover	Trifolium fragiferum	No	Perennial	Spring–summer	10 in.	Fall	0.5–1 lb.	12–15 lb.	Yes	Limited flood tolerance.
New Zealand white clover	Trifolium repans	No	Perennial	Spring–summer	10 in.	Fall	0.5–1 lb.	12–15 lb.	Yes	Tolerates poorly drained soils.
Common vetch	Vicia sativa	No	Annual	Spring–summer	3 ft.	Fall	1–3 lb.	20–30 lb.	Yes	More nectar than other vetches. Seed also less expensive.
Purple vetch	Vicia atropurpurea	No	Annual	April – May spring–summer	2–3 ft.	Fall	1–3 lb.	20–30 lb.	Yes	Not cold tolerant. Best vetch for mild climates.
Alfalfa	Medicago sativa	No	Annual and perennial varieties	Summer	2 ft.	Depends on variety	0.5–2 lb.	15–25 lb.	Yes	Dormant varieties required for cold climates.
Red clover	Trifolium pratense	No	Perennial	Spring–summer	2–3 ft.	Anytime	0.5 lb.	15–20 lb.	Yes	More tolerant of acid soils than other clovers. Short lived
Alsike clover	Trifolium hybridum	No	Perennial	Spring–summer	18 in.	Fall	0.5–2 lb.	15–20 lb.	Yes	Very cold hardy. Performs poorly in warm and dry climates. Short lived.
Purple prairie clover	Dalea purpurea	Yes	Perennial	Mid-summer	1–2 ft.	Fall	0.5–2 lb.	5–10 lb.	Yes	Very adaptable and cold and drought tolerant. Short but prolific blooms. Blooms slightly later than white prairie clover.
White prairie clover	Dalea candida	Yes	Perennial	Mid-summer	1–2 ft.	Fall	0.5–2 lb.	5–10 lb.	Yes	Very adaptable and cold and drought tolerant. Short but prolific blooms. Blooms slightly earlier than purple prairie clover.
Buckwheat	Fagopyrum esculentum	No	Annual	Spring - Summer	1–3 ft.	Spring - Summer	2 lb.	30 lb.	No	Good nurse crop for Phacelia. Excellent source of nest materials for leafcutter bees.
Catmint	Nepeta sp.	No	Perennial	Summer	1–3 ft.	Fall	0.5 lb	10 lb	No	Many varieties, all good nectar plants. Drought tolerant but hard to establish from seed.
Sweet clover	Melilotus officinalis	No	Biennial	Spring–summer	2–6 ft.	Spring - Summer	0.5–1 lb.	12–20 lb.	Yes	Very adaptable.
Showy goldenrod	Solidago speciosa	Yes	Perennial	Fall	4 ft.	Fall	1 oz.	4 lb	No	Good late season forage for cold climates.
New England aster	Aster novae-angliae	Yes	Perennial	Fall	2–4 ft.	Fall	1 oz.	4 lb	No	Good late season forage for cold climates.

1. To convert to metric units, see conversion table, page 156.

D Reducing Bee Poisoning from Pesticides

Eric Mader, *Pollinator Outreach Coordinator, the Xerces Society for Invertebrate Conservation*

Pesticide poisoning of bees usually occurs in one of three different ways:

1. The absorption of toxic chemicals through the bee's exoskeleton;
2. From drinking contaminated nectar; or
3. From eating contaminated pollen during the larval development stage.

Other less common forms of pesticide poisoning can also occur. Leafcutter bees for example can collect contaminated leaf pieces for nest construction. The pesticides covering the leaf are then slowly absorbed by the larvae during development.

Pesticide poisoning often results directly in death. In other cases, however, sub-lethal effects may be observed. Often the nervous system is impacted causing spasms, impaired movement or navigation, and paralysis. Mutations and developmental problems of larvae may also be observed.

While insecticides are the most common culprit in bee poisonings, other agricultural chemicals including various herbicides, fungicides, and plant growth regulators may also have negative effects. Reducing the damage of these chemicals on bees requires an overall reduction of use, control of spray drift, and selection of products with the lowest possible toxicity.

Reducing Pesticide Use

Agricultural practices like crop rotation and the use of resistant crop varieties can reduce the need for pesticides. Monitoring fields for actionable levels of activity rather than routine scheduled spraying is also advised. These are some of the basic strategies of integrated pest management (IPM), a philosophical approach to reducing pesticide use. IPM employs biological and cultural tools in addition to chemicals for the control of crop pests. The objective is to reduce crop damage while still protecting the environment—including beneficial insects like bees. Every agronomic and horticultural crop has industry standard IPM guidelines. You should be familiar with the most current recommendations for your particular crop.

Controlling Spray Drift

Spray drift can occur either as spray droplets or vapors—as happens when a volatile liquid changes to a gas. Factors affecting drift include weather, application method, equipment settings, and spray formulation. Weather-related drift increases with temperature, wind velocity, and convection air currents, as well as during temperature inversions.

Wind-related drift can be minimized by spraying during early morning or in the evening when wind velocity is often lower. However, even a light wind can cause considerable drift. Pesticide labels will occasionally provide specific guidelines on acceptable wind velocities for spraying a particular product.

Midday spraying is also less desirable because as the ground warms, rising air can lift the spray particles in vertical convection currents. These droplets may remain aloft for some time, and can travel many miles. Similarly, during temperature inversions, spray droplets become trapped in a cool lower air mass and move laterally above the ground. Inversions often occur when cool night temperatures follow high day temperatures, and are usually worse in early morning before the ground warms.

Finally, low humidity and high temperatures also promote drift through the evaporation of spray droplets and the corresponding reduction of particle size.

Optimal spray conditions for reducing drift occur when the air is slightly unstable with a minimal steady wind.

Spray application methods and equipment settings also strongly influence the potential for drift. Since small droplets are most likely to drift long distances, aerial applications and mist blowers should be avoided whenever possible. Standard boom sprayers should be operated at the lowest effective pressure and with the nozzles set as low as possible. For example, drop nozzles can be used to deliver insecticides below the tassels if bees are seen foraging on sweet corn pollen.

Nozzle type also has a great influence on the amount of drift a sprayer produces. Turbo jet, raindrop, and air-induction nozzles produce substantially less drift than conventional nozzles. Standard flat fan or hollow cone nozzles are generally poor choices. Select nozzles capable of operating at low pressures (15 to 30 psi) to produce larger, heavier droplets.

Finally, oil-based chemical carriers produce smaller, lighter, droplets than water carriers and should also be avoided when possible. Consider using thickening agents if they are compatible with your pesticide.

Reducing Pesticide Toxicity

While the labels of agricultural chemicals usually list any potential hazards to honey bees, there is usually no information about the hazards to other bees. Application rates that only irritate honey bees may be more harmful to smaller bee species.

Pesticide formulations should be chosen with caution. In general, powders and microencapsulated pesticides tend to be the most harmful to bees. These small particles become trapped along with pollen in the hairs covering a bee's body, and are brought back to the nest as food for the larva. Whenever possible, liquid formulations of equivalent ingredients should be chosen.

Obviously the least toxic chemistry available should always be considered whenever spraying is necessary. For example, pesticides like Bt offer effective control of many pest insects with less harm to most bees. Other chemistry issues to consider include the use of growth regulators for thinning tree fruit instead of products containing carbaryl, and the cautious use of systemic neonicitinoid products like imidacloprid, which may be sequestered in the nectar of flowering plants.

Finally, pesticide toxicity to bees can be reduced by minimizing exposure. Crops should not be sprayed while in bloom if possible and fields should be kept weed free to discourage pollinators from venturing into the crop when it is not in bloom. Night time spraying, when bees are not foraging, is often ideal. Periods of low temperatures may also be good for spraying since many bees are less active. However, the residual toxicity of many pesticides tends to last longer in cool temperatures, so exercise caution.

The following tables list the relative toxicity of many common agricultural chemicals to bees. They are based on information on pesticide labels and information in these publications: Johansen et. al., *Pollinator Protection: A Bee and Pesticide Handbook*; Riedl et. al., *How to Reduce Bee Poisoning From Pesticides*; and Tew, *Protecting Honey Bees from Pesticides*. See the Bibliography, page 149, for more information on these publications. Chemical registrations and formulations change frequently—always check the label for guidelines.

Table D.1
Agricultural Chemicals Highly Toxic to Bees – Do Not Apply to Blooming Crops or Bees

ACTIVE INGREDIENT	RESIDUAL TOXICITY	ACTIVE INGREDIENT	RESIDUAL TOXICITY
2, 4-D		Fonfos	
Abamectin/Avermectrin	3 days	Formetanate HCl	14 hours
Acephate	> 3 days	Gamma-cyhalothrin	> 1 day
Azinphos-Methyl	4 days	Imidacloprid	1 day
Beauveria bassiana	> 1day	Lambda-cyhalothrin	>1 day
Bendiocarb	> 1 day	Lindane	
Bifenthrin	> 1 day	Malathion	3 days for emulsifiable concentrate; 6 days for ultra low volume sprays
Carbaryl	14 days for dusts; 7 days for wettable powders	Methamidophos	5 days
Carbofuran	14 days	Methidathion	3 days
Chloropicrin*		Methomyl	1 day
Chlorpyrifos	7 days	Methyl bromide*	
Clothianidin		Methyl parathion	1 day for emulsifiable concentrate; 8 days for micro-encapsulated
Cyfluthrin	> 1 day	Mevinphos	
Cypermethrin	3 days	Naled	5 days
Cyromazine	> 1 day	Novaluron	
Diazinon	2 days	Oxamyl	2 day
Dichlorvos	>1 day	Oxydemeton-methyl	< 2 hours
Dicrotophos		Permethrin	3 days
Diflubenzuron		Phosmet	5 days
Dimethoate	> 3 days	Pirimiphos-methyl	9 hours
Disulfoton	13 hours	Propoxur	1 day
Endosulfan	3 days	Pyridaben	> 8 hours
Esfenvalerate	1 day	Resmethrin	
Ethion		Spinosad	> 1 day
Fenitrothion		Spirodiclofen	
Fenthion		Tetrachlorvinphos	1 day
Fenoxycarb	1 day	Thiamethoxam	
Fenpropathrin	> 1 day	Thiodicarb	> 8 hours
Fenvalerate	1 day	Zeta-cypermethrin	> 1 day
Fipronil	> 1 day		

* Kills ground-nesting bees

Table D.2 Agricultural Chemicals Moderately Toxic to Bees – Only Apply During Late Evening	
ACTIVE INGREDIENT	**RESIDUAL TOXICITY**
Acetamiprid	
Acetochlor	
Allethrin	
Ametryn	
Azadirachtin	< 2 hours
Bifenazate	
Chlorfenapyr	8 hours
DCPA	
Deltamethrin	< 8 hours
Diatomaceous earth	< 2 hours
Emamectin benzoate	< 2 hours
Fluvalinate	9 hours
Hexythiazox	< 2 hours
Horticultural oils	< 3 hours
Indoxacard	
Mancozeb	
Phorate	< 2 hours (granular)
Pirimicarb	< 2 hours
Potassium salts	
Pymetrozine	2 hours
Pyrethrins	< 2 hours
Pyriproxyfen	< 2 hours
Rotenone	< 2 hours
Sethoxydim	
Tebufenozide	< 8 hours
Temephos	3 hours
Terbufos	
Thiacloprid	
Tralomethrin	< 8 hours
Trichlorfon	14 hours
Triforine	

Table D.3 Agricultural Chemicals with Low Toxicity to Bees	
ACTIVE INGREDIENT	**NOTES**
2, 4-D butoxyethyl ester	
Acequinocyl	
Aldicarb	Granular only, not hazardous when applied more than 4 weeks before bloom
Allenthrin	
Amitraz	
Ammonium thiosulfate	
Azoxystrobin	
Bacillus thuringiensis	
Capsaicin	
Captan	
Carbofuran	Granular only
Chlorpropham	
Chlorpyrifos	Granular only
Copper Sulfate	
Daminozide	
Diazinon	Granular only
Dicofol	
Disulfoton	Granular only
Ethephon	
Ethoprop	Granular only
Fenamiphos	
Garlic	
Gibberellic acid	
Glyphosate	
Indole 3 butyric acid	
Kaolin clay	
Lime-sulfur	
Malathion	Granular only
Metalaxyl	
Methoxyfenozide	
Naphthaleneacetic	
Paraquat	
Propaconazole	
Propargite	
Propoxur	Granular only
Sulfur	
Trifluralin	

Hybrid Nest Blocks for Cavity-Nesting Bees

Eric Mader, *Pollinator Outreach Coordinator, the Xerces Society for Invertebrate Conservation*

Hybrid nest blocks combine the attributes of both solid board nests and the loose-cell management system (figure E.1). Such systems use removable paper inserts for nest liners to facilitate annual nest block cleaning. This is essential to remove disease spores such as chalkbrood and parasites like the hairy-fingered mite. These types of drilled wooden blocks are much more secure and durable than mass-produced plastic and Styrofoam nests. Upon removal, the nest liners can be placed into cold storage and incubated in the same way that loose cells are managed.

Variations of this design are widely used by various leafcutter and mason beekeepers. This particular design uses a compressed foam backing material to prevent the entry of parasites such as chalcid wasps.

Paper nest tubes are custom manufactured by several producers, or as demonstrated here, can be made by rolling precut pieces of paper around a dowel. If paper tubes are not used, some sort of phaseout system should be employed to prevent bees from re-nesting in boards continually without cleaning.

Inter-hole distances should be greater than ½ inch (12.7 millimeters). This distance will result in easier

Eric Mader

Figure E.1 A finished hybrid nest block.

orientation for bees that are returning from foraging. Bees that can easily find their nest hole will complete nests more quickly, and are less likely to enter the wrong nest holes where they could become contaminated with disease spores or parasites. Many commercially available nests tend to have higher hole densities, which can be problematic.

Any of the attributes demonstrated here can be modified, depending on the species being managed. However, the goal should be to configure nest dimensions that promote bee health, maximize female production, and facilitate ease of orientation.

Materials (figure E.2):

- Untreated pine or fir posts, cut to desired length
- Pine or plywood backing board
- Closed-cell packing foam
- Carriage bolts, washers, nuts
- Various tools (drill, saw, hammer, wrench, utility knife, square, propane torch)

For Paper Liners (Optional)

- Dowel or metal rod (slightly smaller than the nest hole diameter)
- Glue
- Paper (newspaper or cooking-type parchment paper)

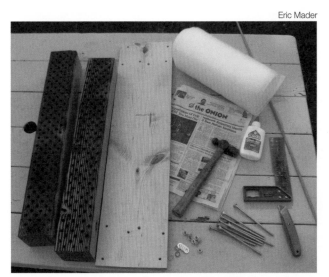

Eric Mader

Figure E.2 Materials and tools needed for hybrid nest block construction.

Nest Block Construction

Untreated 4-inch (10.2-centimeter) fir posts are fine for leafcutter bees. Larger mason bees, such as blue orchard bees and hornfaced bees, require deeper 6-inch (15.2-centimeter) cavities for optimal sex ratios.

Holes are spaced at least ½ inch (1.3 centimeters) apart to reduce search time for nesting bees. Holes can be marked in advance with a pencil and ruler, then started on a drill press. Since most drill presses have a plunge depth less than 3 inches (7.6 centimeters), holes may need to be finished with a hand drill. Brad point drill bits provide the smoothest cut. A backing board should also be used when drilling all the way through to prevent splitting.

Optimal hole diameters are ¼ inch (6.4 millimeters) for alfalfa leafcutter bees, and 5/16 inch (7.9 millimeters) for blue orchard bees. Holes should be drilled slightly larger if paper inserts are to be used.

After drilling, nest blocks are lightly sanded to remove burs. Then the front is scorched with a propane torch (figure E.3). After scorching, the block is

Eric Mader

Figure E.3 Close-up of drilled block.

treated with water-based polyurethane, and the holes are redrilled. Alternately, the nest can be painted in dark contrasting colors such as blue and black; however, some paint finishes tend to be less attractive to bees. Anecdotal evidence suggests that dark colors such as blue and black are most attractive to some cavity-nesting bees.

Backing Materials

A pine or plywood backing board is cut to length, and holes are drilled that correspond to the outer holes on the nest block.

Next a sheet of closed-cell packing foam is trimmed to the size of the backing board. Only closed-cell foam should be used, since it does not absorb water. This type of foam is available from office supply stores (figure E.4).

Assembly

Carriage bolts are inserted through the backing board, foam, and nest block. A hammer may be needed to help seat the bolts the first time the nest is assembled. The bolts are then secured with washers and nuts (figure E.5). By tightening the nuts, the backing foam is compressed, creating a seal that reduces chalcid wasp parasitism. Nesting bees may remove the small exposed circle of foam in the back of the nest cavity; however, the outer seal will remain intact.

Eric Mader

Figure E.4 Backing material (closed-cell packing foam) being cut.

Eric Mader

Figure E.5 Nuts, washers, bolts, drilled block, backing material, and backing board in nest block.

Paper Tube Liners

The use of paper tube liners may reduce the incidence of chalkbrood infections.

Paper tubes can be custom manufactured for this purpose from several commercial vendors, or they can be homemade. Trial and error will determine the exact size paper needed for your application. Once determined, stacked sheets of paper can be trimmed to size using a utility knife (figure E.6).

Paper Tube Assembly

The trimmed paper is wrapped around a dowel or metal rod slightly smaller than the nest block holes (figure E.7). A small drop of glue is added before rolling the paper around the dowel. After rolling the tube, the paper is secured with a thin line of glue, then compressed for several seconds.

Paper Liner Insertion

After the glue has dried, the paper tubes can be inserted into the nest block. It is important that the liner fit tightly within the nest cavity (figure E.8).

Figure E.6 Materials and tools needed to make paper tube liners.

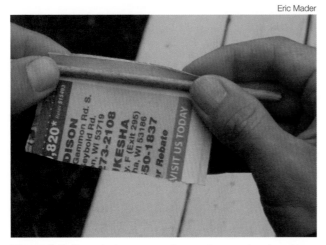

Figure E.7 Paper being wrapped around a wooden dowel to make a paper tube liner.

Figure E.8 Paper tube liner being inserted into nest block.

Any excess space between the liner and nest block can allow movement by parasites.

At the end of the season, the entire nest is disassembled. The foam backing should be discarded, and the paper inserts are carefully removed with tweezers or forceps, or pried out with a small, sharp-pointed awl. The nest block and backing board are then disinfected with a bleach-water solution. The intact paper liners with bees should be stored in a secure location, or placed in cold storage.

Nest Material Comparison for Leafcutter and Mason Bees

Eric Mader, *Pollinator Outreach Coordinator, the Xerces Society for Invertebrate Conservation*

Table F-1
Nest Material Comparison for Leafcutter and Mason Bees

CHARACTERISTICS	STYROFOAM BLOCKS (LOOSE-CELL SYSTEM)	GROOVED LAMINATE BOARDS: WOOD OR STYROFOAM (LOOSE-CELL SYSTEM)	SOLID WOOD BLOCKS (CLOSED-CELL SYSTEM)	REED OR BAMBOO (CLOSED-CELL SYSTEM)	CARDBOARD TUBES (WITH OR WITHOUT PAPER INSERTS)	HYBRID SYSTEM: SOLID WOOD BLOCK WITH REMOVABLE BACK AND PAPER INSERTS
Bee type	Only widely used for leafcutter bees.	Styrofoam laminates used for leafcutter bees. Wood grooved boards used for leafcutters and mason bees.	No longer widely used for leafcutter bees. Small, mason bee versions still used.	Used by some mason bee producers. Not typically used with leafcutters.	Widely used for mason bees. Cardboard and paper tubes historically used for leafcutter bees, no longer common today.	Currently only used for mason bees, but also suitable with leafcutter bees.
Availability	Only produced by a handful of Canadian manufacturers.	Styrofoam laminates only produced by a handful of Canadian manufacturers. Wood laminates commercially produced in small quantities by a few American and Canadian companies; typically they must be homemade.	No longer commercially produced. Older leafcutter blocks occasionally available at farm sales and auctions in western states. Can be made at home.	Bamboo garden stakes are widely available from landscape supply companies and can be cut to length. Phragmites reed is considered invasive in many areas and can be wild collected.	Available from many mason bee suppliers. Custom manufacturing also available from many manufacturers. Sizes for leafcutter bees not commonly available.	Available from several small manufacturers.
Cost	Actual blocks are very low cost; however shipping costs from Canada greatly exceed the cost of the blocks themselves.	Styrofoam laminates are cheap, but like Styrofoam blocks shipping costs from Canada greatly exceed the cost of the boards themselves.	Used leafcutter blocks are moderately priced. Quality lumber to construct new blocks is expensive.	Extremely cheap.	Relatively cheap.	High initial cost to purchase or construct nest block. Low cost for ongoing replacement of paper liners.
Durability	Poor durability. Handling and cell stripping can damage blocks. Rodents and woodpeckers can easily destroy Styrofoam.	Poor durability. Styrofoam laminates have the same problems as Styrofoam. Thin wood laminates easily warp and crack.	Extremely durable. Cracking can be a problem in larger blocks.	Very durable.	Poor durability, prone to crushing, easily damaged by rain, rodents, and birds.	Extremely durable. Cracking can be a problem in larger blocks.
Ability to phaseout nests	Easy to phase out nests since cells are removed annually.	Easy to phase out nests since cells are removed annually.	Difficult; some type of phaseout system is required to prevent bees from nesting in old nest tunnels.	Difficult, some type of phaseout system is required to prevent bees from returning to old nest tunnels.	Easy to do.	Easy to phase out nests since inserts are removed annually.

Table F.1
Nest Material Comparison for Leafcutter and Mason Bees (continued)

CHARACTERISTICS	STYROFOAM BLOCKS (LOOSE-CELL SYSTEM)	GROOVED LAMINATE BOARDS: WOOD OR STYROFOAM (LOOSE-CELL SYSTEM)	SOLID WOOD BLOCKS (CLOSED-CELL SYSTEM)	REED OR BAMBOO (CLOSED-CELL SYSTEM)	CARDBOARD TUBES (WITH OR WITHOUT PAPER INSERTS)	HYBRID SYSTEM: SOLID WOOD BLOCK WITH REMOVABLE BACK AND PAPER INSERTS
Nest block cleaning	Easy to do, by submerging in bleach-water solution.	Easy to do, by submerging in bleach-water solution.	Difficult to clean. Phased out blocks must be redrilled annually, then submerged in bleach-water solution, or heat sterilized.	Impossible to clean. Old tubes should be disposed of annually.	Impossible to clean. Old tubes should be disposed of annually.	Easy to clean by removing used inserts annually. Other disinfection may also be necessary.
Labor	Minimal manual labor if automated cell removers are used.	Moderate manual labor if automated cell removers are used.	Moderate manual labor associated with redrilling, disinfecting, and phasing out old blocks.	Lots of manual labor due to cutting and sorting individual tubes.	Moderate labor sorting, discarding tubes.	Moderate labor sorting, discarding inserts.
Storage	Bulky nest blocks take up a lot of room. Loose cells take up much less cooler space.	Somewhat easier to store than larger blocks. Grooved boards can be disassembled to fit into boxes. Loose cells take up much less cooler space.	Bulky nest blocks take up a lot of room. Bees not removed from the block so the entire nest may need to be refrigerated.	Easy to store. Unused tubes can be stored in boxes; only filled tubes need refrigeration.	Easy to store. Unused tubes can be stored in boxes; only filled tubes need refrigeration.	Bulky nest blocks take up a lot of room. Filled inserts take up much less cooler space.
Weight	Very lightweight.	Styrofoam laminates are very lightweight. Wood grooved boards are heavy.	Heavy.	Generally lightweight.	Moderate weight.	Heavy.
Insulation properties	Very good.	Good.	Very good.	Poor.	Poor.	Good.
Incubation	Easy to do with loose cells.	Easy to do with loose cells.	Difficult—entire block must be incubated. Blocks may warm unevenly.	Relatively easy; entire tube must be incubated.	Relatively easy; entire tube must be incubated.	Easy; inserts can be incubated, or cocoons can easily be removed and incubated.
Sex ratios	Poor. Higher male ratios.	Poor. Higher male ratios.	Okay, but often high male ratios.	Extremely good if tubes are cut to varying lengths. High female ratios.	Okay depending on tube lengths and diameters.	Okay, but often high male ratios.

Parasite control during nesting	Poor. Backing material often fails, allowing parasite entry.	Extremely poor. Backing material often fails, allowing parasite entry. In addition, spaces between boards allow easy access for chalcid wasps.	Very good. Parasites can only enter through nest entrance.	Very good. Parasites can only enter through nest entrance.	Good to poor—depends on how tube backs are sealed and wall thickness.	Good to poor—depends on how tunnel backs are sealed.
Parasite control during storage and incubation	Very poor. Loose cells must be refrigerated to prevent parasite activity. During incubation light traps and other methods must be used to control chalcid wasps.	Very poor. Loose cells must be refrigerated to prevent parasite activity. During incubation light traps and other methods must be used to control chalcid wasps.	Very good. Blocks can also be covered with sawdust or vermiculite during storage.	Very good. Tubes can also be covered with sawdust or vermiculite during storage.	Moderate, tubes should be refrigerated and covered with sawdust or vermiculite during storage.	Poor. Inserts must be refrigerated to prevent parasite activity. During incubation light traps and other methods must be used to control chalcid wasps.
Disease control	Moderate. Nest blocks are cleaned annually, but chalkbrood spores can easily be spread in containers of loose cocoons.	Moderate. Boards are cleaned annually, but chalkbrood spores can easily be spread in containers of loose cocoons.	Very poor. Even with redrilling, and disinfection, it is difficult to kill all chalkbrood spores in wood nests. Second generation leafcutter bees also encourage disease spread in solid block nests.	Good if tubes are phased out annually. Poor if tubes are reused.	Good if tubes are phased out annually. Poor if tubes are reused.	Very good if blocks and backing material are disinfected annually in addition to replacing inserts.
Cocoon inspection	Easy to do with loose cells.	Easy to do with loose cells.	Very difficult. Special probes must be created to remove larvae from nests.	Easy to do by splitting tubes lengthwise using a sharp blade. Tubes can also be X-rayed.	Easy if paper inserts are used inside cardboard. Moderately easy to take apart cardboard tubes if no inserts are used. Tubes can also be X-rayed.	Easy to take apart paper inserts.
Drying of cells and pollen	Poor drying ability. Wet pollen, leaf tissue, and cocoons subject to mold growth.	Poor drying ability in Styrofoam laminates. Wet pollen, leaf tissue, and cocoons subject to mold growth. Wood boards are fine.	Very good. Wood porosity reduces mold growth. Overdrying of pollen provisions can be a problem in new lumber.	Good. Porosity reduces mold growth. Tubes may become too dry in some areas however.	Okay. Cardboard and paper tend to dry quickly, and may wick moisture from pollen. Paraffin-coated straws solve this problem. Plastic straws should not be used.	Okay. Paper inserts tend to dry quickly, and may wick moisture from pollen. Paraffin-coated straws solve this problem. Plastic straws should not be used.

Nest Material Comparison for Leafcutter and Mason Bees (continued)

CHARACTERISTICS	STYROFOAM BLOCKS (LOOSE-CELL SYSTEM)	GROOVED LAMINATE BOARDS: WOOD OR STYROFOAM (LOOSE-CELL SYSTEM)	SOLID WOOD BLOCKS (CLOSED-CELL SYSTEM)	REED OR BAMBOO (CLOSED-CELL SYSTEM)	CARDBOARD TUBES (WITH OR WITHOUT PAPER INSERTS)	HYBRID SYSTEM: SOLID WOOD BLOCK WITH REMOVABLE BACK AND PAPER INSERTS
Processing damage to cocoons	Potentially high if cell strippers are not properly adjusted.	Potentially high if cell strippers are not properly adjusted.	No damage to bees.	No damage to bees.	No damage to bees.	No damage to bees unless inserts are shaken during development, or crushed.
Bee appeal	Low.	Low appeal for Styrofoam laminates. Higher appeal for wood boards.	Relatively high appeal to bees.	Very appealing to bees—bamboo more so than reed.	Moderately appealing.	Moderately appealing.
Bee orientation	Poor. Few orientation marks for returning foragers. Especially when blocks are not painted, and do not have raised orientation patterns.	Okay. Better when boards are painted with orientation patterns.	Okay. Better when blocks are painted with orientation patterns.	Excellent. Irregular tube lengths and sizes provide many orientation "landmarks" for bees returning to nest.	Poor. Better when tubes are painted different colors, or vary in size and length.	Okay. Better when blocks are painted with orientation patterns.
Scalability	High. Large numbers of bees can be managed and produced using this system. Limiting factors will be parasite control—especially chalcid wasps. Bee health and sex ratios will never be optimal. Other necessary loose-cell equipment such as cell strippers add significantly to the cost.	High. Large numbers of bees can be managed and produced using this system. Limiting factors will be parasite control—especially chalcid wasps. Bee health and sex ratios will never be optimal. Other necessary loose-cell equipment such as cell strippers add significantly to the cost.	Moderate. Equipment is easy to manage and maintain. Limiting factors will be disease control—especially chalkbrood. Short-term results may be good, but long-term prospects are poor. Expect annual losses after several seasons.	Low. Smaller numbers of very healthy bees, with good female to male ratios can be produced this way. Limiting factors will involve management labor—especially sorting, cutting, and phasing out tubes.	Moderate. Medium-sized populations of bees can be produced this way. Limiting factors will be management labor associated with sorting, and phasing out tubes, and controlling parasites, especially chalcid wasps.	Moderate. This system can produce medium-sized populations of healthy bees. Labor associated with storing and sorting paper inserts, controlling chalcid wasps during storage and incubation, and nest block cleaning will be limiting factors.

G IPM for Beekeepers

Eric Mader, *Pollinator Outreach Coordinator, the Xerces Society for Invertebrate Conservation*

Regardless of what bee species you keep, a significant amount of beekeeping involves controlling parasites and disease.

Integrated Pest Management (IPM) is a set of principles used in agriculture to control pests and diseases in the most effective and sustainable way possible.

As a beekeeper, IPM requires that you do four things:

1. Constantly monitor the health of your bees—frequently checking for parasites and signs of disease.
2. Determine when to respond—it is unreasonable to expect zero parasites in your bee population. *Action is only taken when the cost of the potential damage exceeds the cost of the treatment.*
3. Use the simplest, least toxic treatment first.
4. Use a variety of treatment practices to control problems.

Pest-control methods fall into three categories that can be thought of as a pyramid:

CHEMISTRY

GENETICS

CULTURAL PRACTICES

Cultural practices are the foundation of the pyramid, and they should be the foundation of your pest control system. Specifically cultural practices are the physical ways in which you exclude parasites and diseases. Examples include using screened bottom boards on honey bee hives to reduce varroa mites; using light traps to control chalcid wasps in stored mason bees; and using new, clean nest materials every year in bumble bee boxes.

Good genetics are the second line of defense in maintaining bee health. Genetics refers to the breeding stock of your bee population. Are your bees adapted to your local climate? If you keep honey bees, are they bred for hygienic behavior? Are you using a univoltine strain of leafcutter bees to reduce chalkbrood? Univoltine strains produce one generation per year.

Chemistry is the treatment of last resort. Chemicals may control parasites and disease, but they also may weaken bees, and they discourage the development of bees' natural defense mechanisms. Bee parasites may also develop resistance to the chemicals used against them, making them even harder to kill in the future. Canadian leafcutter beekeepers routinely use chemicals like dichlorvos to control parasites during incubation. And many US honey beekeepers are dependent on medications like Fumagillin and Terramycin to control diseases such as *Nosema* and foulbrood, respectively.

By always using the best cultural practices available, and relying on good bee genetics, chemical use can be minimized.

Finally, remember that stress is the underlying cause of many parasite and disease problems. The types of stress that managed bees face tend to fall into five categories:

1. Pesticide poisoning
2. Crowding
3. Inadequate shelter (poor apiary sites, wet conditions, extreme temperatures)
4. Old, unsanitary nest materials
5. Lack of food

Control these five stress factors, follow the four principles of IPM for beekeepers, use appropriate pest and disease treatments—and your bees will thrive!

Additional Resources

Bees and Alternative Beekeeping Equipment

Bee Diverse

Based in British Columbia, Web retailer Bee Diverse offers a variety of backyard mason bee nests for sale, along with informational books and videos.

641 Claremont St.
Coquitlam, BC
Canada V3J 3T5
(800) 794-2144
http://www.beediverse.com

Entomo-Logic

Entomo-Logic is a Washington-based company providing the Western subspecies of the blue orchard bee, as well as mason bee nests. Their bees are inspected for parasites and diseases before shipment.

21323 232nd St. SE
Monroe, WA 98272-8982
(360) 863-8547
http://www.entomologic.com

Forked Tree Ranch

Sells blue bottle flies for managed pollination.

HCR 60, Box 226
Porthill, ID 83853
(208) 267-2632
http://www.forkedtreeranch.com

International Pollination Systems

Provides pollination consulting and research.

http://www.pollination.com/

Jonesville Paper Tube Corporation

A custom cardboard and paper tube manufacturer, Jonesville Paper Tube has extensive experience providing materials for mason bee nests. The company provides free sample materials upon request.

540 Beck St.
PO Box 39
Jonesville, MI 49250
(517) 849-9963
http://www.papertube.com

JWM Leafcutters

JWM buys and sells alfalfa leafcutter bees, and nest equipment. They also provide loose-cell removal and nest block cleaning. Based in Idaho and Canada.

4300 S. Chicago St.
Nampa, ID 83686-8949
(208) 467-1488
http://www.jwmleafcutters.com

Knox Cellars

A Washington-based company providing the western subspecies of the blue orchard bee and mason bee nests.

25724 NE 10th St.
Sammamish, WA 98074
(206) 849-5065
http://www.knoxcellars.com

Koenders Manufacturing Ltd.

A Canadian-based agricultural manufacturer, Koenders produces plastic leafcutter bee shelters, nest materials, incubation trays, and loose-cell harvesting equipment.

PO Box 171
105 Main St.
Englefeld, SK
Canada S0K 1N0
(877) 581-8877
http://www.koendersmfg.com

Mason Bee Homes

Sells small, backyard-style mason bee houses.

2460 Oakes Rd.
Black Creek, BC
Canada V9J 1J1
http://www.masonbeehomes.com

Midori Horticultural Services

Sells several species of mason bees, leafcutter bees, and offers managed pollinator consulting.

http://www.midorihorticultural.com

North Star Seed Ltd.

A Canadian supplier of leafcutter bees and leafcutter management equipment.

Box 2220
Neepawa, MB
Canada, R0J 1H0
(204) 476-5241
http://www.northstarseed.com

Osmia.com

A Web site selling the Western subspecies of the blue orchard bee. Based in Utah.

http://www.osmia.com

Pollinator Paradise

A manufacturer of leafcutter and mason bee nest blocks.

The Pollinator Paradise Web site has extensive informational articles on leafcutter and mason bee management.

31140 Circle Dr.
Parma, ID 83660
http://www.pollinatorparadise.com

Conservation Resources

Agrecol

Agrecol is a midwestern producer of native prairie seed. They specialize in grasses and wildflowers native to the northern tall grass prairie, and have experience in natural area restoration. Many of their seed mixes are suitable for pollinator conservation projects.

2918 Agriculture Dr.
Madison, WI 53718
(609) 226-2544
http://www.agrecol.com

Ecological Society of America

The ESA's Pollinator Tool Kit provides fact sheet-type informational resources on pollinator conservation.

1707 H. St. NW., Suite 400
Washington, DC 20006
(202) 833-8773
http://www.esa.org/ecoservices

JF New

A native plant nursery and ecological consulting firm based in Indiana. JF New offers over 355 plant species including tall grass prairie plants (both seeds and plugs), as well as native trees. Many of their plants are suitable for pollinator conservation projects.

708 Roosevelt Road
Walkerton, IN 46574
(574) 586-3400
http://www.jfnew.com

Prairie Nursery

A producer of native tall grass prairie seeds and flats of live plants. Based in Wisconsin.

PO Box 306
Westfield, WI 53964
800 Gro-Wild
http://www.prairienursery.com

The Xerces Society

The Xerces Society's pollinator program works with farmers, land managers, public agencies, and gardeners to promote the conservation and recovery of native pollinator insects and their habitat. To accomplish those goals Xerces produces user-friendly publications on how to protect, restore, and enhance habitat for pollinators (including Farming for Bees, *and the* Pollinator Conservation Handbook). *Xerces also provides training events—including workshops, farm walks, and seminars—to provide a first-hand look at specific pollinator conservation issues.*

4828 SE Hawthorn Blvd.
Portland, OR 97215
(503) 232-6639
http://www.xerces.org

Informational Web Sites

Bee Tools

A service of the Luckiamute Beekeeping Supply, the Bee Tools Web site provides articles and construction plans relating to bumble bee and mason beekeeping, as well as informational articles on the commercial honey bee pollination business in the Pacific Northwest.

http://members.aol.com/beetools/

Bumble Boosters

A cooperative project of the University of Nebraska Department of Entomology, the Lincoln Public Schools Science Focus Program, and the Folsom Children's Zoo. Bumble Boosters provides a free downloadable bumble bee identification guide and links to bumble bee related information.

http://bumbleboosters.unl.edu

Discover Life

Identification keys for countless plants and animals—including thousands of pollinators. Includes extensive photos and distribution maps for many bees, wasps, butterflies, flies, and other insects.

http://www.discoverlife.org

Insect Visitors of Prairie Wildflowers in Illinois

Provides descriptions of various insect groups common to tall grass prairie ecosystems, including many pollinators. Includes a list of insect records for many common native plants.

http://www.illinoiswildflowers.info

How to Manage the Blue Orchard Bee

The electronic version of the classic book written by William Kemp and Jordi Bosch. The most comprehensive treatise written on the subject of mason bee management. A publication of the USDA Sustainable Agriculture Research and Education program.

http://www.sare.org/publications/bee/blue_orchard_bee.pdf

National Biological Information Infrastructure

A Department of the U.S. Geological Survey, the NBII Pollinators Project provides extensive links to informational articles on pollinator conservation, insect identification, and pollination related news articles. The site also includes information on pending government initiatives and legislative activities that affect pollinator conservation.

http://nbii.gov

North American Bee Mites

A project to identify and classify parasitic mites of native and introduced bee pollinators.

http://insects.ummz.lsa.umich.edu/beemites/

The Pollination Home Page

Maintained by a beekeeper and updated infrequently, this has extensive pictures of bees and informational articles on beekeeping and pollination.

http://www.pollinator.com

Saskatchewan Alfalfa Seed Producers Association

Extensive informational articles on leafcutter bee management including a number of excellent pictorial guides to various bee diseases.

http://www.saspa.com/beeManagement.htm

The University of Minnesota Bee Lab

Information on honey beekeeping courses, including online and weekend short-courses at the University of Minnesota. Includes information resources on maintaining healthy honey bees.

http://www.extension.umn.edu/honeybees/

What's That Bug?

An incredible site operated by amateur entomologists. What's That Bug provides countless photos and information on insects. WTB relies on photo submissions from the public and provides assistance identifying invertebrates of all types. The site has excellent photos of many pollinators native to North America.

http://www.whatsthatbug.com/

Wild Blueberry Growers Guide

Maintained by the University of Maine Cooperative Extension, this site has several excellent fact sheets on managing leafcutter bees, wild mason bees, bumble bees, and honey bees for blueberry pollination.

http://wildblueberries.maine.edu/TOC.htm

Bibliography

Arbury, J., R. Bird, M. Honour, C. Innes, and M. Salmon. 1997. *The Complete Book of Plant Propagation*. Taunton. Newtown, CT.

Baker, H. G. and I. Baker. 1983. A brief historical review of the chemistry of floral nectar. In *The Biology of Nectaries*. B. Bentley and T. Elias (eds.) Columbia University Press. New York, NY.

Baird, C. and R. Bitner. 1980. *Raising Leafcutting Bee-Tips for Small Producers*. University of Idaho. Extension Bulletin No. 527.

Baird, C. and R. Bitner. 1991. *Loose Cell Management of Alfalfa Leafcutting Bees in Idaho*. University of Idaho. Extension Bulletin No. 588.

Baird, C., D. Mayer, and R. Bitner. 1991. *Pollinators in Alfalfa Seed Production and Pest Management*. Western Regional Extension Publication 12.

Batra, S. 1979. *Osmia cornifrons* and *Pithitis smaragdula*, two Asian bees introduced into the United States for crop pollination. Proceedings of the IVth International Symposium on Pollination. Maryland Agricultural Experimentation Station. Miscellaneous Publications 1: 307–312.

Batra, S. 1998. Hornfaced bees for apple pollination. *American Bee Journal* 138: 364–365.

Batra, S. 1994. *Anthophora pilipes villosula* Sm. (Hymenoptera: Anthophoridae), a manageable Japanese bee that visits blueberries and apples during cool, rainy, spring weather. Proceedings of the Entomological Society of Washington 96: 98–119.

Batra, S. 1997. Solitary Bees for Orchard Pollination. http://www.pollinatorparadise.com/Solitary_Bees/Solitar.htm

Bekey, R. and E. C. Klostermeyer. 1981. *Orchard Mason Bee*. Washington State University. Extension Bulletin 922.

Bosch, J. and W. Kemp. 1999. Exceptional cherry production in an orchard pollinated with blue orchard bees. *Bee World* 80: 163–173.

Bosch, J., W. Kemp, and S. S. Peterson. 2000. Management of *Osmia lignaria* (Hymenpotera: Megachilidae) populations for almond pollination: methods to advance bee emergence. *Environmental Entomology* 29: 874–883.

Bosch, J. and W. Kemp. 2001. *How to Manage the Blue Orchard Bee*. USDA-SARE. Handbook Series Book 5.

Buchmann, S. 1983. Buzz pollination in angiosperms. In *Handbook of Experimental Pollination Biology*. C.E. Jones and R. J. Little (eds.), Van Nostrand Reinhold. New York, NY.

Buchmann, S. and G. Nabhan. 1996. *The Forgotten Pollinators*. Island Press. Washington, DC.

Camazine S., J. L. Deneubourg, N. R. Franks, J. Sneyd, G. Theraulaz, and E. Conaceau. 2001. *Self-Organization in Biological Systems*. Princeton University Press. Princeton, NJ.

Cane, J. 2005. Squash pollinators of the Americas Survey (SPAS). http://www.ars.usda.gov/Research/docs.htm?docid=12041

Capon, B. 1990. *Botany for Gardeners*. Timber Press. Portland, OR.

Caron, D. 1999. *Honey Bee Biology and Beekeeping*. Wic-Was Press. Cheshire, CT.

Carvell, C., D. Roy, S. Smart, R. Pywell, C. Preston, and D. Goulson. 2006. Declines in forage availability for bumblebees at a national scale. *Biological Conservation* 132: 481–489.

Committee on the Status of Pollinators in North America. 2007. *Status of Pollinators in North America*. The National Academies Press. Washington, D.C. http://www.nap.edu

Conrad, R. 2007. *Natural Beekeeping: Organic Approaches to Modern Apiculture*. Chelsea Green Publishing. White River Junction, VT.

Cummings, Dan. Cummings-Violich, Inc. Personal communication.

Cook, R. and L. Calvin. 2005. Greenhouse tomatoes change the dynamics of the North American fresh tomato industry. Economic Research Report No. ERR-2. http://www.ers.usda.gov/publications/err2/

Danforth, B. Bee Phylogeny at Cornell University http://www.entomology.cornell.edu/BeePhylogeny/

DeGrandi-Hoffman, G. and J. Watkins. 2000. The foraging activity of honey bees (*Apis mellifera* L.) and non-*Apis* bees on hybrid sunflowers (*Helianthus annuus* L.) and its influence on cross-pollination and seed set. *Journal of Apicultural Research* 39: 37–45.

De Guzman, L., T. Rinderer, and A. Frake. 2007. Growth of *Varroa destructor* (Acari: Varroidae) populations in Russian honey bee (Hymenoptera: Apidae) colonies. *Annals of the Entomological Society of America* 100: 187–195.

Delaplane, K. and D. Mayer. 2000. *Crop Pollination by Bees*. CABI Publishing. New York, NY.

Dogterom, M. 2002. *Pollination with Mason Bees: a Gardener and Naturalists' Guide to Managing Mason Bees for Fruit Production*. Beediverse Publishing. Coquitlam, BC.

Eickwort G., J. Eickwort, J. Gordon, and M. Eickwort. 1996. Solitary behavior in a high-altitude population of the social sweat bee *Halictus rubicundus* (Hymenoptera: Halictidae). *Behavioral Ecology and Sociobiology* 38: 227–233.

Evans, E., I. Burns, and M. Spivak. 2007. *Befriending Bumble Bees: a Practical Guide to Raising Local Bumble Bees*. University of Minnesota Extension. Saint Paul, MN.

Evans, E. and M. Spivak. 2006. Effects of honey bee (Hymenoptera: Apidae) and bumble bee (Hymenoptera: Apidae) presence on cranberry (Ericales: Ericaceae) pollination. *Journal of Economic Entomology* 99: 614–620.

Eves, J. 1970. Biology of *Monodontomerus obscurus* Westwood, a parasite of the alfalfa leafcutting bee, *Megachile rotundata* (Fabricius) (Hymenoptera: Torymidae; Megachidae). *Melanderia* 4: 1–18.

Eves, J., D. Mayer, and C. Johansen. 1980. *Parasites, predators and nest destroyers of the alfalfa leafcutting bee*, Megachile rotundata. Washington State University. Extension Publication 32.

Foster. K., T. Wenseleers, and F. Ratnieks. 2005. Kin selection is the key to altruism. *Trends in Ecology and Evolution* 21: 57–60.

Frazier, M. 2000. *Pollination Contracts*. Publication 5.4. Mid-Atlantic Apicultural Research and Extension Consortium. Pennsylvania State University. University Park, PA.

Free, J. 1993. *Insect Pollination of Cultivated Crops*. Academic Press. London, UK.

Furgala B., M. Spivak, and G. Reuter. 2000. *Beekeeping in Northern Climates: Short Course Manual*. Minnesota Extension Service Distribution Number: PC-7553-S.

Greenleaf, S. and C. Kremen. 2006. Wild bees enhance honey bees' pollination of hybrid sunflower. Proceedings of the National Academy of Science 103: 13890–13895.

Goulson, D., M. Hanley, B. Darvill, and J. Ellis. 2006. Biotope associations and the decline of bumblebees (*Bombus* spp.). *Journal of Insect Conservation* 10: 95–103.

Griffin, B. 1999. *The Orchard Mason Bee: The Life History, Biology, Propagation, and Use of a North American Native Bee*. Knox Cellars Publishing. Bellingham, WA.

Hallett, P. 2001. A Method for 'Hiving' Solitary Bees and Wasps. *American Bee Journal* 141: 133–136.

Hanlin, S. and S. McClurg. 2003. *Blue Bottle Fly* (Calliphora sp.*) Rearing Procedures*. NCRPIS. Ames, IA.

Harbo, J. and J. Harris. 1999. Selecting honey bees for resistance to *Varroa jacobsoni*. *Apidologie* 30: 183–196.

Harbo, J. and J. Harris. 2005. Suppressed mite reproduction explained by the behavior of adult bees. *Journal of Apicultural Research* 44: 21–23.

Harris, J., and T. Rinderer. 2004. *Varroa* resistance of hybrid ARS Russian honey bees. *American Bee Journal* 144: 797–800.

Heitkam, Pat. Heitkam's Honey Bees, Orland, CA. Personal communication.

Heinrich, B. and M. Heinrich. 1983. Size and caste in temperature regulation by bumblebees. *Physiological Zoology* 56: 552–562.

Hobbs, G. 1981. *Alfalfa leafcutter bees for pollinating alfalfa in western Canada*. Agriculture Canada Publication 1495.

Homan, H., L. Kish, N. Waters, and R. Bitner. *Alfalfa Leafcutting Bee Management in Idaho*. University of Idaho. Extension Bulletin 538.

Hopkins, I. 1914. *History of the Bumblebee in New Zealand: Its Introduction and Results*. New Zealand Department of Agriculture Industrial and Commercial Bulllletin 46.

Ibrahim, A. and M. Spivak. 2006. The relationship between hygienic behavior and suppression of mite reproduction as honey bee (*Apis mellifera*) mechanisms of resistance to *Varroa destructor*. *Apidologie* 37: 31–40.

Ibrahim, A., G. Reuter, and M. Spivak. 2007. Field trial of honey bee colonies bred for mechanisms of resistance against *Varroa destructor*. *Apidologie* 38: 67–76.

Johansen, C. 1973. *Leafcutting Bee Storage*. Washington State University. Extension Bulletin No. 2909.

Johansen, C., J. Eves, and C. Baird. 1973. *Control of Alfalfa Leafcutting Bee Enemies*. Washington State University. EM 2631.

Johansen, C. and D. Meyer. 1990. *Pollinator Protection: a Bee and Pesticide Handbook*. Wicwas Press. Cheshire, UK.

Jones, R. and P. Munn. 1998. *Habitat Management For Wild Bees and Wasps*. International Bee Research Association. Cardiff, UK.

Kearns, C. and J. Thomson. 2001. *The Natural History of Bumblebees: a Sourcebook for Investigations*. University Press of Colorado. Boulder, CO.

Kemp, W. and J. Bosch. 2001. Bees in your backyard. *American Bee Journal* 141: 183–185.

Kish, L., H. Homan, and N. Waters. *Chalkbrood—a Serious Disease of the Alfalfa Leafcutting Bee*. University of Idaho. Current Information Series 477.

Koerber, T. and J. Medler. 1958. A trap-nest survey of solitary bees and wasps in Wisconsin, with biological notes. *Transactions of the Wisconsin Academy of Sciences, Arts and Letters* 47: 53–63.

Krombein, K. 1962. Natural history of Plummers Island, Maryland. XVI. Biological notes on *Chaetodactylus krombeini* Baker, a parasitic mite of the megachilid bee *Osmia* (Osmia) *lignaria* Say (Acarina: Chaetodatylidae). Proceedings of the Biological Society of Washington 75: 237–249.

Krombein, K. 1967. *Trap-nesting Wasps and Bees: Life Histories, Nests and Associates*. Smithsonian Press. Washington, DC.

Loose, J., F. Drummond, C. Stubbs, S. Woods, and S. Hoffman. 2005. *Conservation and Management of Native Bees in Cranberry*. University of Maine: Maine Agricultural and Forest Experiment Station. Technical Bulletin 191.

Lovgren, S. 2005. Mayan beekeeping tradition fades. National Geographic News. http://news.nationalgeographic.com/news/2005/06/0628_050628_maya_bees.html

Macior, L. 1975. The pollination ecology of *Delphinium tricorne* (Ranunculaceae). *American Journal of Botany* 62: 1009–1016.

McFrederick, S. and G. LeBuhn. 2006. Are urban parks refuges for bumble bees *Bombus* spp. (Hymenoptera: Apidae)? *Biological Conservation* 129: 372–382.

McGregor, S. 1976. *Insect Pollination of Cultivated Crop Plants.* Agricultural Handbook No. 496. Agricultural Research Service. U.S. Department of Agriculture.

Maeta, Y. 1990. Utilization of wild bees. *Farming Japan* 24: 13–19.

Mameko-bachi Kenkyu-jo. 2003. Homepage. http://park1.wakwak.com/~mameko-bachi/

Manitoba Forage Seed Association. 2003. Pollination and leafcutting bees. http://www.forageseed.mb.ca/Articles/pollinationLeafBees.htm

Matheson, A. 1994. *Forage for Bees In An Agricultural Landscape.* International Bee Research Association. Cardiff, UK.

Medler, J. 1967. Biology of *Osmia* in trap nests in Wisconsin (Hymenoptera: Megachilidae). *Annals of the Entomological Society of America* 60: 338–344.

Medler, J. and J. Lussenhop. 1968. *Leafcutter Bees of Wisconsin.* University of Wisconsin Research Bulletin. Vol. 274.

Meyer, R. and D. McBride. 1989. *Alfalfa Seed Production and Leafcutting Bee Management.* North Dakota State University. Extension Bulletin No. 54.

Michener, C. 1974. *The Social Behavior of the Bees: a Comparative Study.* Harvard University Press. Cambridge, MA.

Michener, C. 2000. *The Bees of the World.* The Johns Hopkins University Press. Baltimore, MD.

Michener, C., R. McGinley, and B. Danforth. 1994. *The Bee Genera of North and Central America (Hymenoptera: Apoidea).* Smithsonian Institution Press. Washington, DC.

Mitchell, T. 1962. *Bees of the Eastern United States.* North Carolina Agricultural Experiment Station Technical Bulletin 152.

Morse, R. and N. Calderone. 2000. The value of honey bees as pollinators of U.S. crops in 2000. *Bee Culture Magazine.* A.I. Root Company. Medina, OH.

Morse, R. and K. Flottum (eds.). 1997. *Honey Bee Pests, Predators and Diseases.* 3rd edition. A.I. Root Company. Medina, OH.

O'Toole, C. and A. Raw. 1991. *Bees of the World.* Blanford Publishing. London, UK.

Ozkan, H. E. 2000. *Reducing Spray Drift.* Ohio State University Extension Bulletin. 816-00. Columbus, OH.

Parker, F. and D. Frohlich. 1983. Hybrid sunflower pollination by a manageable Composite specialist: the sunflower leafcutter bee (Hymenoptera: Megachildae). *Environmental Entomology* 2: 576–581.

Parker, F. and P. Torchio. 1980. Management of wild bees. In *Beekeeping in the United States.* USDA Agriculture Handbook 335.

Phillips, J. and E. Klostermeyer. 1978. Nesting behavior of *Osmia lignaria propinqua* Cresson. *Journal of the Kansas Entomological Society* 51: 91–108.

Poinar, G. and B. Danforth. 2006. A fossil bee from early cretaceous Burmese amber. *Science* 314: 614.

Proctor, M., P. Yeo, and A. Lack. 1996. *The Natural History of Pollination.* Timber Press. Portland, OR.

Queller, D. and J. Strassmann. 1998. Kin selection and social insects. *BioScience* 48: 165–175.

Rank, G. 2005. An improved leafcutting bee for increased alfalfa seed production. University of Saskatchewan. http://www.leafcuttingbees.com

Riedl, H., L. Johansen, and J. Barbour. 2006. *How to Reduce Bee Poisoning From Pesticides.* Oregon State University. Corvallis, OR. PNW 591. http://extension.oregonstate.edu/catalog/pdf/pnw/pnw591.pdf

Richards, K. 1989. *Alfalfa Leafcutter Bee Management in Western Canada.* Agriculture Canada. Publication 1495/E.

Robinson, W., R. Nowodrodzki, and R. Morse. 1989. The value of honey bees as pollinators of U.S. crops. *American Bee Journal* 129: 411–423, 477–487.

Roulsten, T. and J. Cane. 2000. Pollen nutritional content and digestibility for animals. In *Pollen and Pollination*. A. Dafni, M. Hesse, E. Pacini (eds.) Springer. Vienna.

Rust, R. 1974. The systematics and biology of the genus *Osmia*, subgenera *Osmia*, *Chalcosima* and *Cephalosmia* (Hymenoptera: Megachilidae). *Wasmann Journal of Biology* 32: 1–93.

Sammataro, D. and A. Avitabile. 1998. *The Beekeeper's Handbook*. 3rd edition. Cornell University Press. Ithaca, NY.

Sarospataki, M., J. Novak, and V. Molnar. 2005. Assessing the threatened status of bumble bee species (Hymenoptera : Apidae) in Hungary, Central Europe. *Biodiversity and Conservation* 14: 2437–2446.

Seeley, T. 1989. The honey bee colony as a superorganism. *American Scientist* 77: 546–553.

Seeley, T. 1995. *The Wisdom of the Hive: the Social Physiology of Honey Bee Colonies*. Harvard University Press. Cambridge, MA.

Seeley, T. 2007. Honey bees of the Arnot Forest: a population of feral colonies persisting with *Varroa destructor* in the northeastern United States. *Apidologie* 38: 19–29.

Seeley, T. and P. Visscher. 2004. Group decision-making in nest selection by honey bees. *Apidologie* 35: 101–116.

Shepherd, M., S. Buchmann, M. Vaughan, and S. Hoffman Black. 2003. *Pollinator Conservation Handbook*. Xerces Society. Portland, OR.

Sladen, F. 1989. *The Humble-Bee: Its Life-History and How to Domesticate It*. Logaston Press. UK

Spivak, M. 1996. Honey bee hygienic behavior and defense against *Varroa jacobsoni*. *Apidologie* 27: 245–260.

Spivak, M. and D. Downey. 1998. Field assays for hygienic behavior in honey bees (Apidae: Hymenoptera). *Journal of Economic Entomology* 91: 64–70.

Spivak, M. and G. Reuter. 1993. *Successful Queen Rearing Short Course Manual*. Department of Entomology and Minnesota Extension Service Distribution # MI6346. (educational packet Dist. # EP6347)

Spivak, M. and G. Reuter. 1998. Performance of hygienic honey bee colonies in a commercial apiary. *Apidologie* 29: 291–302.

Spivak, M. and G. Reuter. 2000. Honey bee diseases and pests. Minnesota Extension Service Distribution Number BU-7554-S.

Spivak, M. and G. Reuter. 2001. Resistance to American foulbrood diseases by honey bee colonies *Apis mellifera* bred for hygienic behavior. *Apidologie* 32: 555–565.

Spivak, M. and G. Reuter. 2001. *Varroa destructor* infestation in untreated honey bee (Hymenoptera: Apidae) colonies selected for hygienic behavior. *Journal of Economic Entomology* 94: 326–331.

Spivak, M. and G. Reuter. 2005. *A Sustainable Approach to Controlling Honey Bee Diseases and Varroa Mites*. SARE Agricultural Innovations-03AGI2005 Fact Sheet. www.sare.org/publications/factsheet/0305. htm

Spivak, M. and G. Reuter. 2007. Web course "Healthy Bees" http://www.extension.uvm.edu/elms/

Stanghellini, M., J. Tambrose, and J. Schultheis. 2002. Diurnal activity, floral visitation and pollen deposition by honey bees and bumble bees on field-grown cucumber and watermelon. *Journal of Apicultural Research* 41: 27–34.

Stephen, W. and J. Undurraga. 1978. *Chalkbrood Disease in the Leafcutting Bee*. Oregon State University. Bulletin 630.

Stubbs, C., F. Drummond, and D. Yarborough. 2002. *How to Manage Alfalfa Leaf Cutting Bees for Wild Blueberry Pollination*. University of Maine. Extension Fact Sheet No. 300.

Tew, J. E. 1997. *Protecting Honey Bees from Pesticides*. Ohio State University. Extension Factsheet HYG-2161-97.

Torchio, P. 1972. *Sapyga pumila* Cresson, a parasite of *Megachile rotundata* (Hymenoptera: Sapygidae, Megachilidae) II. Methods for control. *Melanderia* 10: 23–30.

Torchio, P. 1976. Use of *Osmia lignaria* Say as a pollinator in an apple and prune orchard. *Journal of the Kansas Entomological Society* 49: 475–482.

Torchio, P. 1979. An eight-year field study involving control of *Sapyga pumila* Cresson (Hymenoptera: Sapygidae), a wasp parasite of the alfalfa leafcutting bee, *Megachile pacifica* Panzer. *Journal of the Kansas Entomological Society* 52: 412–419.

Torchio, P. 1985. Field experiments with the pollinator species *Osmia lignaria propinqua* Cresson, in apple orchards. *Journal of the Kansas Entomological Society* 58: 448–464.

Torchio, P. 1987. Use of non-honeybee species as pollinators of crops. Entomological Society of Ontario 119: 111–124.

Torchio, P. 1989. In-nest biologies and development of immature stages of three *Osmia* species. *Annals of the Entomological Society of America* 82: 599–615.

Torchio, P. 1989. Biology, immature development, and adaptive behavior of *Stelis montana*, a cleptoparasite of *Osmia*. *Annals of the Entomological Society of America* 82: 616–632.

Torchio, P. 1990. *Osmia ribifloris*, a native bee species developed as a commercially managed pollinator of highbush blueberry (Hymenoptera: Megachilidae). *Journal of the Kansas Entomological Society* 63: 427–436.

Torchio, P. 1991. Use of *Osmia lignaria propinqua* as a mobile pollinator of orchard crops. *Environmental Entomology* 20: 590–596.

Torchio, P. 1991. Bees as crop pollinators and the role of solitary species in changing environments. *Acta Horticulturae* 288: 49–61.

Torchio, P. 1992. Effects of spore dosage and temperature on pathogenic expressions of chalkbrood syndrome caused by *Ascophaera torchioi* within larvae of *Osmia lignaria propinqua*. *Environmental Entomology* 21: 1086–1091.

Torchio, P. and J. Bosch. 1992. Biology of *Tricrania stansburyi*, a meloid beetle cleptoparasite of the bee *Osmia lignaria propinqua* (Hymenoptera: Megachilidae). *Annals of the Entomological Society of America* 85: 713–721.

Traynor, J. 1993. *Almond Pollination Handbook For Almond Growers And Beekeepers*. Kovak Books. Bakersfield, CA.

Vaughan, M. and S. H. Black. 2006. *Agroforestry: Sustaining Native Bee Habitat for Crop Pollination*. Agroforestry Note 32. USDA, NRCS and FS. USDA National Agroforestry Center. http://www.unl.edu/nac/agroforestrynotes/an32g06.pdf

Vaughan, M. and S. H. Black. 2006. *Agroforestry: Improving Forage for Native Bee Crop Pollinators*. Agroforestry Note 33. USDA, NRCS and FS. USDA National Agroforestry Center. http://www.unl.edu/nac/agroforestrynotes/an33g07.pdf

Vaughan, M. and S. H. Black. 2006. *Enhancing Nest Sites for Native Bee Crop Pollinators*. Agroforestry Note 34. USDA, NRCS and FS. USDA National Agroforestry Center. http://www.unl.edu/nac/agroforestrynotes/an34g08.pdf

Vaughan, M., M. Shepherd, C. Kremen, and S. Hoffman Black. 2007. *Farming for Bees: Guidelines for Providing Native Bee Habitat on Farms*. 2nd edition. The Xerces Society for Invertebrate Conservation. Portland, OR.

Walstrom, R. 1974. *Alfalfa Leafcutting Bee Management for Alfalfa Pollination in South Dakota*. South Dakota State University. Extension Bulletin No. 544.

Waters, N., H. Homan, and C. Baird. 1980. *Recognizing Insect Enemies of Alfalfa Leafcutting Bees*. University of Idaho. CIS 163.

Webster T., and K. Delaplane (eds.). 2001. *Mites of the Honey Bees*. Dadant and Sons, Inc. Hamilton, IL.

Williams, P. 1998. An annotated checklist of bumble bees with an analysis of patterns of description (Hymenoptera: Apidae, Bombini). *Bulletin of The Natural History Museum, Entomology* 67: 79–152.

Willmer, P., A. Bataw, and J. Hughes. 1994. The superiority of bumblebees to honeybees as pollinators: insect visits to raspberry flowers. *Ecological Entomology* 19: 271–284.

Wilson, E. 2005. Kin selection as the key to altruism: its rise and fall. *Social Research* 72: 159–166.

Wilson, E. and B. Hölldobler. 2005. Eusociality: origin and consequences. Proceedings of the National Academy of Sciences 102: 13367–13371.

Winter, K., L. Adams, R. Thorp, D. Inouye, L. Day, J. Ascher, and S. Buchmann. 2006. *Importation of Non-Native Bumble Bees into North America: Potential Consequences of Using* Bombus terrestris *and other Non-Native Bumble Bees for Greenhouse Crop Pollination in Canada, Mexico, and the United States.* North American Pollinator Protection Campaign. White Paper.

Winston, M. 1987. *The Biology of the Honey Bee*. Harvard University Press. Cambridge, MA.

Wisconsin Agricultural Statistics Service. 2005. Cranberry Production and Pollination Survey. http://www.nass.usda.gov/Statistics_by_State/Wisconsin/Publications/Crops/cranpollination.pdf

Yamada, M. 1990. Control of *Chaetodactylus* mite, *Chaetodactylus nipponicus* Kurosa, an important mortality agent of hornfaced bee, *Osmia cornifrons* Radoszkowski. Aomori Apple Experiment Station Bulletin 26: 39–77.

Zayed, A., D. Roubik, and L. Packer. 2004. Use of diploid male frequency data as an indicator of pollinator decline. Proceedings of the Royal Society of London B. (Supplement) 271: S9–S12.

Zayed, A. and L. Packer. 2005. Complementary sex determination substantially increases extinction proneness of haplodiploid populations. Proceedings of the National Academy of Science 102: 10742–10746.

Conversions

US UNIT	MULTIPLY BY	SI UNIT
inches	25.4	millimeters
feet	0.305	meters
yards	0.914	meters
miles	1.61	kilometers
acres	0.405	hectars
square feet	0.093	square meters
ounces	28.4	grams
pounds	0.454	kiligrams
gallons*	3.79	liters
gallons*	0.004	cubic meters
TEMPERATURE		
$°F = (°C*9/5) + 32$		
$°C = (°F - 32) * 5/9$		

* Loose alfalfa leafcutter bee cells are normally stored in feed sacks and sold by the gallon. A gallon of loose cells is approximately 10,000 dormant bees. It may not be a gallon by volume.

Acknowledgments

This book was produced with support from the U.S. Department of Agriculture's Sustainable Agriculture Research and Education (SARE) program; the University of Minnesota Department of Entomology; and The Xerces Society for Invertebrate Conservation.

Photos and line drawings in this book were contributed by the authors and their colleagues. Contributors are credited at the top right corner of photos and line drawings.

The authors thank the following persons for their review of the manuscript and helpful suggestions: Dewey M. Caron, Professor Emeritus, Department of Entomology and Wildlife Ecology, University of Delaware; Mark Doudlah, President, the Agrecol Corporation; Robert Kane, Biological Science Technician, USDA Agricultural Research Service; Dena Leibman, Communications Specialist, SARE; Evan A. Sugden, Department of Biology, University of Washington; Robbin Thorp, Professor Emeritus, Department of Entomology, University of California-Davis; Mace Vaughan, Conservation Director, The Xerces Society for Invertebrate Conservation; and Todd West, Assistant Professor of Horticulture, West Virginia University.

Holly Hyde, NRAES Editor, assisted with peer review and copyediting. Marty Sailus, NRAES Director, edited the manuscript and managed the project from peer review to printing.

About the Authors

As National Pollinator Outreach Coordinator at The Xerces Society for Invertebrate Conservation, Eric Mader works to raise awareness of native pollinator conservation techniques among growers and government agencies. He is also an Assistant Professor of Extension at the University of Minnesota's Department of Entomology. His previous work includes commercial beekeeping and crop consulting for the native seed industry. Eric maintains a unique menagerie of bees, including honey bees and several species of leafcutter and mason bees. His beekeeping interests include alternative hive and nest systems, urban beekeeping, and selective breeding.

Marla Spivak is Professor and Extension Entomologist at the University of Minnesota. Her interest in bees and beekeeping was kindled while working for a commercial beekeeper when she was 18. Her PhD, obtained at the University of Kansas, involved a two-year study of the ecology of Africanized bees in Costa Rica. Her current research goals are to protect the health of bee pollinators and to promote sustainable beekeeping practices. Her combined research, teaching, and extension appointment allows her to explore basic questions related to honey bee behavioral ecology, neuroethology, and mechanisms of disease resistance and to translate results directly to students, beekeepers, and the public. Her current research focuses on the antimicrobial activity and benefits of propolis (plant-derived resins that bees collect and apply as caulk within their nest cavities) on diseases and the immune systems of honey bees. She is grateful to her graduate students, who encouraged her to promote studies of native bee pollinators, and in so doing, to promote the ecology, health, and aesthetics of urban and rural landscapes.

Elaine Evans is a bee biologist and conservationist working to promote healthy native bee populations. She completed her MS in entomology at the University of Minnesota, where she studied the impact of floral resource competition between honey bees and bumble bees. She also studied tomato and cranberry pollination and established a bumble bee-rearing program at the University of Minnesota's Bee Lab. Elaine is the co-author of *Befriending Bumble Bees: A Guide to Raising Local Bumble Bees*. She currently works as a Conservation Consultant with The Xerces Society for Invertebrate Conservation, where she has created field guides for threatened bumble bees and co-authored a review of the population status of three species of imperiled North American bumble bees.

About PALS

Plant and Life Sciences Publishing (PALS) is a program of the Department of Horticulture in the College of Agriculture and Life Sciences (CALS) at Cornell University. PALS assists university faculty and their colleagues in publishing, marketing and distributing books for small farmers, gardeners, land owners, workshops, college courses, and consumers. The University of Maine and West Virginia University are partners.

PALS books are practical and comprehensive. They are based on decades of grower experience and university research. Book categories include garden and landscape, small-scale farming, small-fruit production, composting, pasture-based livestock production, rural-land management and personal finance. The gardening, small-scale farming, small-fruit production, rural-land management and pasture-based livestock production books were written for the Northeast, Mid-Atlantic and Great-Lakes states and adjoining Canadian provinces. Most contain knowledge that will be useful to a wider audience.

Visit PALS web site for descriptions of books distributed.

Plant and Life Sciences Publishing (PALS)

34 Plant Science
Ithaca, New York 14853

Phone: (607) 255-7654
Fax: (607) 254-8770
E-mail: palspublishing@cornell.edu
Web site: PALSPUBLISHING.COM
Marty Sailus, PALS Director

About SARE

SARE
Sustainable Agriculture
Research & Education

SARE is a grant making and outreach program. Its mission is to advance—to the whole of American agriculture—innovations that improve profitability, stewardship and quality of life by investing in groundbreaking research and education. Since it began in 1988, SARE has funded more than 5,500 projects around the nation that explore innovations, from managing alternative pollinators to cover crops to myriad other best practices. Administering SARE grants are four regional councils composed of farmers, ranchers, researchers, educators and other local experts. Coordinators in every state and island protectorate run education programs for ag professionals, and SARE Outreach publishes practical books, bulletins, online resources, and other information for farmers and ranchers. All of SARE's activities are funded by the National Institute of Food and Agriculture, U.S. Department of Agriculture.

For more information about SARE's grants program and information products, visit www.sare.org or contact:

SARE Outreach
1122 Patapsco Building
University of Maryland
College Park, MD 20742-6715
info@sare.org • (301) 405-7955

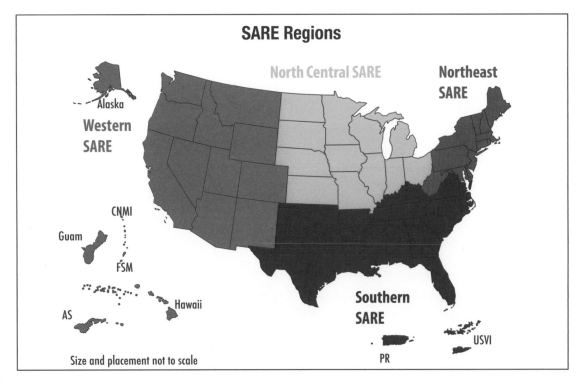

SARE's four regional offices and outreach office work to advance
sustainable innovations to the whole of American agriculture.